PRENTICE HALL LITERATURE

PENGUIN EDITION

Teaching Resources

Unit 4
Rebels and Dreamers

The British Tradition

PEARSON

Prentice Hall

Upper Saddle River, New Jersey
Boston, Massachusetts

Pearson Prentice Hall™ is a trademark of Pearson Education, Inc.
Pearson® is a registered trademark of Pearson plc.
Prentice Hall® is a registered trademark of Pearson Education, Inc.

ISBN 0-13-165321-0

3 4 5 6 7 8 9 10   10 09 08 07

Contents

UNIT 4

Introduction to *Frankenstein* by Mary Wollstonecraft Shelley

Poetry of William Wordsworth

"The Rime of the Ancient Mariner" and "Kubla Khan"
by Samuel Taylor Coleridge

"She Walks in Beauty," from *Child Harold's Pilgrimage* and from *Don Juan*
by George Gordon, Lord Byron

"Ozymandias," "Ode to the West Wind," and "To a Skylark"
by Percy Bysshe Shelley

Poetry of John Keats

"Speech to Parliament" by George Gordon, Lord Byron

"A Song: 'Men of England'" by Percy Bysshe Shelley

"On the Passing of the Reform Bill" by Thomas Babington Macaulay

"On Making an Agreeable Marriage" by Jane Austen

from *A Vindication of the Rights of Woman* by Mary Wollstonecraft

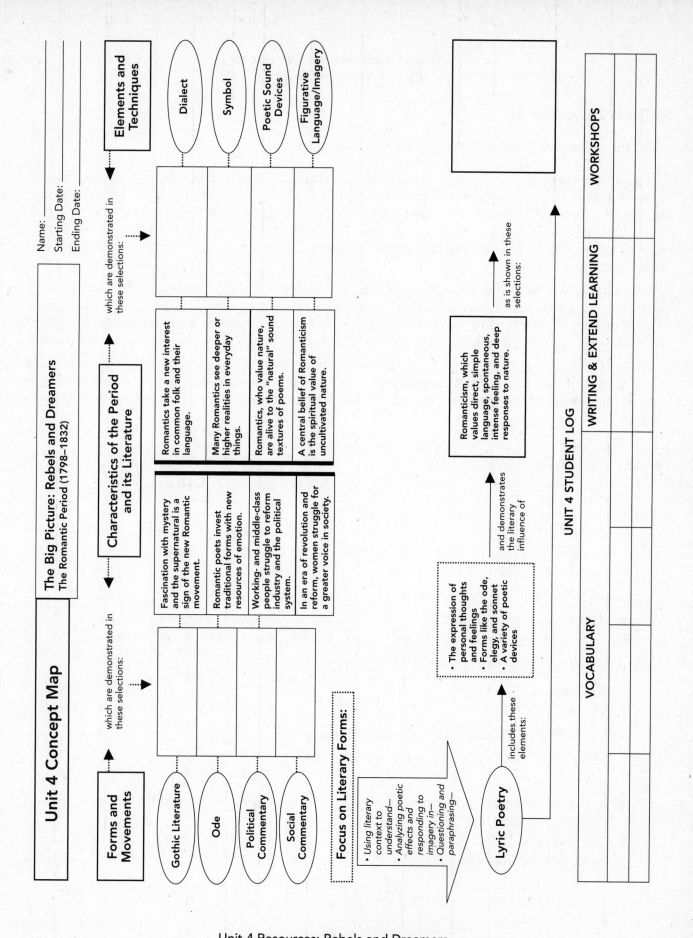

Unit 4 Concept Map

Name:
Starting Date:
Ending Date:

The Big Picture: Rebels and Dreamers
The Romantic Period (1798–1832)

which are demonstrated in these selections:

Characteristics of the Period and its Literature

Fascination with mystery and the supernatural is a sign of the new Romantic movement.

Romantic poets invest traditional forms with new resources of emotion.

Working- and middle-class people struggle to reform industry and the political system.

In an era of revolution and reform, women struggle for a greater voice in society.

Romantics take a new interest in common folk and their language.

Many Romantics see deeper or higher realities in everyday things.

Romantics, who value nature, are alive to the "natural" sound textures of poems.

A central belief of Romanticism is the spiritual value of uncultivated nature.

Elements and Techniques

- Dialect
- Symbol
- Poetic Sound Devices
- Figurative Language/Imagery

which are demonstrated in these selections:

Forms and Movements

- Gothic Literature
- Ode
- Political Commentary
- Social Commentary

Focus on Literary Forms:

- Using literary context to understand—
- Analyzing poetic effects and responding to imagery in—
- Questioning and paraphrasing—

Lyric Poetry

includes these elements:

- The expression of personal thoughts and feelings
- Forms like the ode, elegy, and sonnet
- A variety of poetic devices

and demonstrates the literary influence of

Romanticism, which values direct, simple language, spontaneous, intense feeling, and deep responses to nature.

as is shown in these selections:

UNIT 4 STUDENT LOG

VOCABULARY

WRITING & EXTEND LEARNING

WORKSHOPS

Unit 4: Rebels and Dreamers
Diagnostic Test 7

MULTIPLE CHOICE

Read the selection. Then, answer the questions that follow.

In a modern society that relies so little on the oral tradition, it is hard to fathom the importance of griots, but they played an important role in ancient Mali. Griots served as the oral historians in that fourteenth-century African empire, passing stories down from one generation to the next. The griots told tales, sang, and played musical instruments. Their special knowledge of history allowed them to work as advisors to kings, mediate disputes, arrange social events, and observe and report on important events such as battles.

Griots often told the stories of kings, such as Sundiata, the legendary Lion King, who had been cruelly persecuted as a child. Griots also told the tale of Mansa Musa, the king who greatly expanded Mali's empire and made the city of Timbuktu a center of learning. The stories of Sundiata and Mansa Musa are still told today. Most of what people know about the past kings of Mali comes from these griot tales.

The role of the griot in today's society is different than it was in ancient times. Today's griots are actors, performers, and announcers. Music is especially important in their work, and the music of modern griots, such as Kasse Mady Diabete, moves the listener with its mix of ancient tradition and modern innovation.

1. Which of the following best describes a fourteenth-century griot?
   A. a musician and performer
   B. an advisor
   C. a storyteller and musician
   D. an oral historian

2. What was the most important task of the griot?
   A. to help the king rule
   B. to pass down stories from one generation to the next
   C. to entertain the king
   D. to advise others

3. Which of the following were kings about whom griots told stories?
   A. Mansa Musa and Sundiata
   B. Sundiata and the Lion King
   C. the Lion King and Mali
   D. Mansa Musa and Timbuktu

4. Which of the following is true of Sundiata?
   A. He was a famous griot.
   B. He was persecuted as a child.
   C. He expanded the Mali empire.
   D. He established Timbuktu.

5. Who established Timbuktu as a center of learning?
   A. the griots
   B. Mali
   C. Sundiata
   D. Mansa Musa

6. Which of the following is the best explanation of why the role of oral historian is less important for modern griots?
   A. There are no longer kings in Mali.
   B. Society has grown much larger.
   C. History is written down today.
   D. Entertainment is now more important.

7. What is the role of griots in modern society?
   A. to report important events
   B. advisors to rulers
   C. performers and musicians
   D. to arrange social events

Read the selection. Then, answer the questions that follow.

The history of Ancient Rome is rife with important military campaigns, many of which were conducted by Julius Caesar. One of Caesar's most famous conquests was Gaul, a region that now makes up France and parts of Germany. In one battle, Caesar's troops were outnumbered nearly six to one. His forces were able to defeat the Gauls, however, due in large part to the Romans' extraordinary discipline. Even the bravest Gallic chieftain feared Caesar's assaults.

Not all of Caesar's campaigns were successful, however. While warring with the Gauls, Caesar made expeditions to Britain, but was forced to withdraw after a series of fierce attacks by Celtic tribes.

One constant difficulty for both the Gallic and Roman forces was a lack of food. As a result, after one hard-fought, late-summer victory, Caesar and his army spent time gorging on the plentiful food available during the harvest time.

The Roman conquest of Gaul had a marked effect on the development of European culture that can still be felt today. For example, the breadth of the Roman Empire allowed the Latin language to spread throughout much of Europe. Today's "Romance" languages, such as French, Spanish, and Italian, still show Latin's heavy linguistic influence. In addition, the Roman legal system has inspired and influenced legal systems throughout the western world. The Romans also built roads throughout their empire that were in use for centuries and are, in some cases, still in use today!

8. Which of the following is true of Julius Caesar?
   A. He was an important Roman conqueror.
   B. He ruled Gaul.
   C. He conquered Britain.
   D. He had few important victories.

9. Which of the following was Caesar's most famous conquest?
   A. Britain
   B. Gaul
   C. Rome
   D. Germany

10. Who defended Britain from Julius Caesar's invasion?
    A. Gallic warriors
    B. Celtic tribes
    C. Roman forces
    D. British armies

11. Which of the following best explains why Julius Caesar was considered a great general?
    A. His troops were well-disciplined and were able to win against great odds.
    B. Even though he suffered many losses, he never gave up fighting.
    C. He was well-liked and able to keep his men well-fed.
    D. He was the first Roman to conquer the heavily-fortified isle of Britain.

12. What constant difficulty did Julius Caesar face in his Gallic campaign?
    A. providing warm clothing for his men
    B. feeding his army
    C. identifying enemy spies
    D. keeping weapons in good condition

13. What great advantage did Julius Caesar have over the fierce Gallic warriors?
    A. the good nutrition of his troops   **C.** the strict discipline of his troops
    B. the numbers of his troops   **D.** the loyalty of his troops

14. Which of the following languages were influenced by the ancient Romans?
    A. Romance languages   **C.** Germanic languages
    B. Celtic languages   **D.** Gallic languages

15. Which of the following is a long-lasting result of Roman conquests?
    A. the Italian state   **C.** the establishment of Germany
    B. legal systems in the western world   **D.** the system of European highways

Unit 4 Introduction
Names and Terms to Know

A. DIRECTIONS: *Match each name or term on the left with its fact on the right. Write the letter of the fact on the line before the name or term it defines.*

Names and Terms	**Facts**
___ 1. French Revolution	A. conservative party in Parliament, dominated by large landowners and aristocrats
___ 2. Bastille	B. literary movement that prized nature and the pure simplicity of the past
___ 3. Reign of Terror	C. technological and economic shift in which machinery and factories assumed new importance
___ 4. Industrial Revolution	D. rebellion that began on July 14, 1789
___ 5. Tories	E. French philosopher who championed the freedom of human nature
___ 6. Whigs	F. reform-minded party in Parliament, dominated by the middle class
___ 7. Romanticism	G. Paris prison for political prisoners
___ 8. Jean-Jacques Rousseau	H. violent phase of the French Revolution, during which the Jacobins gained power

B. DIRECTIONS: *Write an additional fact about each of the following names and terms.*

1. Reign of Terror: _____

_____

2. Whigs: _____

_____

3. Romanticism: _____

_____

4. Jean-Jacques Rousseau: _____

_____

Name _____ Date _____

Focus Questions

DIRECTIONS: *Use the hints below to help you answer the focus questions. You will find all of the information in the Unit Introduction in your textbook.*

1. What was the impact of the French Revolution on England?
   Hint: How did British intellectuals, such as William Wordsworth, feel at first about the ideals of the French Revolution? _____

   _____

   _____

   Hint: How did the Reign of Terror affect British public opinion? _____

   _____

   _____

2. What was the situation of the working class during this period?
   Hint: What were some of the problems resulting from the Industrial Revolution? _____

   _____

   _____

   Hint: How did British society at this time seem to be split into two angry, opposing camps?

   _____

   _____

   Hint: How did the Whig victory in 1830 affect factory safety? _____

   _____

   _____

3. In what ways does the literature of this period reflect its political and social realities?
   Hint: What kinds of subject matter did Wordsworth and Coleridge use in their poetry?

   _____

   _____

   Hint: How did the "second generation" of Romantics—Byron, Shelley, and Keats—react toward British conservatism? _____

   _____

   _____

Study these words from the selections. Then, complete the activities that follow.

Word List A

companion [kuhm PAN yuhn] *n.* one who keeps company with another
The dog was a <u>companion</u> to the elderly woman.

compared [kuhm PAYRD] *v.* examined to note similarities or differences
We <u>compared</u> prices in order to find the least expensive product.

impudence [IM pyoo dins] *n.* rudeness; disrespect
The <u>impudence</u> of the girl's reply startled her mother.

notion [NOH shuhn] *n.* an impulse or whim
Sarah had a <u>notion</u> to call her grandmother at the last minute.

schemes [SKEEMZ] *n.* plans (especially clever, secret, or devious ones)
The robbers planned many different <u>schemes</u> to break into the store.

social [SOH shuhl] *adj.* having to do with living in a community
It is important to achieve a balance between one's work and <u>social</u> life.

trouble [TRUB uhl] *n.* distress; problems
The thunderstorm created floods that caused much <u>trouble</u> for drivers.

union [YOON yuhn] *n.* a state of being united or in agreement
The <u>union</u> of the two countries made both of them stronger.

Word List B

bare [BAYR] *adj.* undisguised; naked
The lack of furnishings of the apartment made it feel <u>bare</u> and empty.

bashfully [BASH fuhl lee] *adv.* timidly; in a shy manner
The shy girl hid <u>bashfully</u> behind the tree.

dearest [DEER est] *adj.* most valued
I have known one of my <u>dearest</u> friends since childhood.

grieve [GREEV] *v.* mourn; feel sorrow
The little boy will <u>grieve</u> if his sick hamster dies.

patient [PAY shuhnt] *adj.* being willing to wait for something
It is important to be <u>patient</u> when you are applying for jobs.

pouch [POWCH] *n.* a small bag used for carrying items
The cowboy put his supplies into a <u>pouch</u> that he carried on his saddle.

prospects [PRAH spekts] *n.* possibilities
The experiment's <u>prospects</u> for success were high.

waste [WAYST] *n.* something that has been destroyed or is no longer useful
The bombing of the city laid <u>waste</u> to its great buildings.

Selected Poetry of Robert Burns and Joanna Baillie
Vocabulary Warm-up Exercises

Exercise A *Fill in each blank in the paragraph below with the appropriate word from Word List A. Use each word only once.*

Stan suddenly had the [1] _____ that his friend, Joe, was upset with him.

He [2] _____ Joe's recent behavior to the way he acted in the past. Stan

suspected that Joe was jealous of his new [3] _____, a small dog named

Rocky. Stan spent a great deal of time with Rocky in order to help him deal with the

[4] _____ he had in adjusting to his new surroundings. However, the

more time that Stan spent with Rocky, the more Joe's [5] _____ toward

Stan increased. Stan noticed that in [6] _____ situations, such as par-

ties, Joe would ignore him. Stan was upset about this situation, and he devised many

[7] _____ that he hoped would solve this problem. He hoped to achieve a

[8] _____ of his old friend and his new one.

Exercise B *Decide whether each of the following statements is true or false. Circle T or F, and explain your answers.*

1. Your <u>dearest</u> possession is what you value least.
   T / F _____

2. When you <u>grieve</u>, you laugh a great deal.
   T / F _____

3. A <u>pouch</u> is useful for carrying things.
   T / F _____

4. If your arm is uncovered, it is <u>bare</u>.
   T / F _____

5. You need to be <u>patient</u> if you want to grow a plant.
   T / F _____

6. You need to behave <u>bashfully</u> if you are trying to get noticed.
   T / F _____

7. A public dump would be filled with piles of <u>waste</u>.
   T / F _____

8. You need to evaluate your <u>prospects</u> before you decide on a career.
   T / F _____

Name _____ Date _____

Reading Warm-up A

Read the following passage. Pay special attention to the underlined words. Then, read it again, and complete the activities. Use a separate sheet of paper for your written answers.

Romanticism was not a fleeting <u>notion</u> in the late-eighteenth and nineteenth centuries. It was a movement that lasted a long time and that rejected the ideas of order, calm, and balance, and rejection of nature that were typical of the <u>social</u> ideas of that time.

When Romantic works are <u>compared</u>, it can be seen that the Romantics held very specific views about nature and the individual. The Romantics believed in a <u>union</u> of people with nature. This idea was a direct opposite of the <u>impudence</u> that many great thinkers of the time felt about nature. These thinkers did not have respect for nature and believed that nature had an evil power over man.

The Romantics believed that the main <u>trouble</u> in their society could be found in the fact that the individual was not appreciated. They felt that this was a problem because a person's personality deserved to be examined. Some Romantics worked to develop <u>schemes</u> to help others appreciate people's individuality. They believed that these plans would make many problems in society disappear. This view was simple and easy to understand for many people who lived during this time. As a result, Romanticism quickly became popular.

Furthermore, Romanticism rejected the use of formal rules, especially as they applied to the arts. This rejection is evident in the many new artistic styles that flourished during this period.

As a movement, Romanticism had no <u>companion</u> or peer in its variety and impact on the world. It quickly reached all corners of the globe because its emphasis on the individual appealed to common people everywhere. In fact, its influence is still felt in the arts.

1. Underline the words that explain why Romanticism was not a fleeting <u>notion</u>. Tell what *notion* means.

2. Circle the words that tell what were typical <u>social</u> ideas of that time. If a young man has a boring *social* life, what might he do to make it better?

3. Underline the phrase that tells what can be seen when Romantic works are <u>compared</u>. Tell what *compared* means.

4. Circle the phrase that tells the type of <u>union</u> in which Romantics believed. For what purpose might students in your school form a *union*?

5. Underline the phrase that tells what <u>impudence</u> means. Use *impudence* in a sentence.

6. Circle the word in a nearby sentence that means about the same as <u>trouble</u>. Give an example of one kind of *trouble* some modern societies have.

7. Underline the word in a nearby sentence that means about the same as <u>schemes</u>. What is an example of a career that involves coming up with *schemes*?

8. Circle the word that means about the same as <u>companion</u>. Use *companion* in a sentence.

Selected Poetry of Robert Burns and Joanna Baillie
Reading Warm-up B

Read the following passage. Pay special attention to the underlined words. Then, read it again, and complete the activities. Use a separate sheet of paper for your written answers.

Carl looked around him and exhaled slowly with pleasure. From the small <u>pouch</u> attached to his belt, he removed a book of poetry and a sandwich. He found a spot on the <u>bare</u> ground underneath a large, shady oak tree and made himself comfortable.

It was a beautiful day to be outside in the midst of nature, and Carl was actively engaged in reading, one of his <u>dearest</u> pleasures. It was a sunny spring day. The fragrance of blooming flowers wafted through the air, relaxing him and making him slightly drowsy.

Carl continued reading, pausing occasionally to take a bite of the sandwich. He soon became aware of a small bird in the grass nearby; it was staring at his sandwich, <u>patient</u> and calm, hoping for some crumbs. Throwing away his leftovers would be a <u>waste</u> since that little bird was waiting so quietly for a crust of bread. Carl tore off a piece and tossed it to the timid little animal, which cautiously snapped up the bread and moved quickly away.

Almost immediately, more birds appeared as if by magic, sensing the <u>prospects</u> or chances of a free meal. Smiling at their antics, Carl tore off tiny bits of bread, trying to be sure that each bird got at least one piece. However, a particularly aggressive bird kept snatching bits of bread away from the others until they angrily chased it away. Carl knew he would not <u>grieve</u> for that mean bird missing out on the rest of the bread. Soon, the sandwich was gone and the birds flew away, one at a time, until only the first little bird was left, peeking timidly and <u>bashfully</u> at him from a low branch of the tree. Carl smiled at his shy little friend and went contentedly back to reading.

1. Underline the words that tell what Carl removed from his <u>pouch</u>. Tell what a **pouch** is.

2. Underline the phrase that tells what Carl did on the <u>bare</u> ground. Describe what **bare** ground looks like.

3. Circle the word that tells what one of Carl's <u>dearest</u> pleasures is. What is a word or phrase that means about the same as **dearest**?

4. Circle a phrase in a nearby sentence that explains what <u>patient</u> means. What is a situation in which a small child might have trouble being **patient**?

5. Underline the phrase that tells what would be a <u>waste</u>. Tell what **waste** means.

6. Circle the word that means about the same as <u>prospects</u>. Use **prospects** in a sentence.

7. Underline the words that tell for what Carl would not <u>grieve</u>. What is an example of something that would make most people **grieve**?

8. Circle the word that means about the same as <u>bashfully</u>. Describe what a person looks like when he or she is behaving **bashfully**.

10

"To a Mouse" and **"To a Louse"** by Robert Burns
"Woo'd and Married and A'" by Joanna Baillie
Literary Analysis: Dialect

Robert Burns was one of the first poets to write verse that incorporated the Scottish dialect of English. **Dialect** is the language, chiefly the speech habits and patterns, of a particular social class, region, or group. Usually dialect differs from the standard form of the language because it possesses its own unique grammar, pronunciation, and vocabulary.

In "To a Mouse," Burns's use of dialect adds to the poem's appeal and the reader's appreciation. If the poem had been written in standard English, it would lack the sense of immediacy and the color achieved in such lines as:

That wee bit heap o' leaves an' stibble, / Has cost thee mony a weary nibble!

By using Scottish dialect, Burns succeeded in capturing his people's tenderness for and intimacy with nature and their shared acceptance of the prospect of "nought but grief an' pain" in the wake of "promised joy."

DIRECTIONS: *The following lines are from "To a Mouse." Rewrite each line in standard English and explain the effect that the use of Scottish dialect alone can achieve.*

1. "Wee, sleekit, cow'rin', tim'rous beastie,"

   _____

   _____

   _____

2. "A daimen icker in a thrave / 'S a sma' request:"

   _____

   _____

   _____

3. "An' naething, now, to big a new ane,"

   _____

   _____

   _____

4. "To thole the winter's sleety dribble, / An' cranreuch cauld!"

   _____

   _____

   _____

"**To a Mouse**" and "**To a Louse**" by Robert Burns
"**Woo'd and Married and A'**" by Joanna Baillie

Reading Strategy: Translate Dialect

A **dialect** is the language and speech habits of the members of a particular group, class, or region. Each dialect has its own unique grammar, pronunciation, and vocabulary. Robert Burns and Joanna Baillie wrote their poems in the Scottish dialect of English. Their use of dialect made their poems more accessible and familiar to their contemporaries in Scotland. Modern readers can use a number of different strategies to **translate dialect:**

- Read footnotes to get definitions.
- Use context to guess meaning.
- Speak words aloud and listen for similarities to standard English words.
- Look for similarities between printed dialect words and English words.
- Note apostrophes, which often signal that a letter has been omitted.

DIRECTIONS: *After reading the following lines from "To a Mouse," translate each word in italics, identifying the strategy you used to determine each word's meaning.*

1. "I wad be laith to *rin* an' chase thee / Wi' murd'ring pattle."

   _____

   _____

   _____

2. "I doubt na, *whyles*,[8] but thou may thieve;"

   _____

   _____

   _____

3. "Thy wee bit *housie,* too, in ruin!"

   _____

   _____

   _____

4. "An' *lea'e* us nought but grief an' pain,"

   _____

   _____

   _____

[8]whyles: At times.

"To a Mouse" and **"To a Louse"** by Robert Burns
"Woo'd and Married and A'" by Joanna Baillie
Vocabulary Builder

Using the Suffix -*some*

A. DIRECTIONS: *The following words all contain the suffix*—some, *meaning "having specific qualities." Using the word's context along with what you know about this suffix, write a definition of each italicized word in the blank.*

1. At first the jokes were funny, but they became *tiresome.*

   _____

2. When Jerome went to the zoo, he thought the snakes were *loathsome*, but Janelle enjoyed them.

   _____

3. Bees abuzzing around your head at a picini are so *bothersome*, aren't they?

   _____

Using the Word List

dominion	impudence	winsome
discretion	inconstantly	

B. DIRECTIONS: *Write a word from the Word List to answer each question.*

1. Which word means most nearly the opposite of *imprudence?* _____

2. If you observe someone acting rudely toward a stranger, what word might you use to describe such behavior? _____

3. Which word is closest in meaning to *changeably?* _____

4. Which word describes a monarch's authority over his or her subjects?

   _____

5. What word might you use to describe a person who has a charming manner and appearance? _____

"**To a Mouse**" and "**To a Louse**" by Robert Burns
"**Woo'd and Married and A'**" by Joanna Baillie

Grammar and Style: Interjections

An **interjection** is a word or phrase that can stand by itself and that is used to express emotion. Consider these examples from "To a Louse."

My sooth! right bauld ye set your nose out. . . .

O, Jenny, dinna toss your head. . . .

Notice that an exclamation mark often follows an interjection to show the strong emotion being expressed.

A. PRACTICE: *Underline the interjection in each sentence.*

1. My gosh! There's a bug in that woman's hair.
2. Hey! It's only a louse.
3. Good grief! You say that as if a louse were nothing at all to have in your hair.
4. Aha! It's not a louse—it's a bee!
5. Yikes! I remember when a bee flew into my mother's hair while she was driving.
6. I didn't think she would stop the car in time! Whew! It was close.

B. Writing Application: *For each of the following interjections, write a sentence that incorporates it. Punctuate each interjection by using an exclamation mark.*

1. well

_____

2. hurrah

_____

3. hey

_____

4. alas

_____

5. whoa

_____

6. oh

_____

7. my goodness

_____

Name _____ Date _____

"To a Mouse" and "To a Louse" by Robert Burns
"Woo'd and Married and A'" by Joanna Baillie
Support for Writing

Use the Venn diagram below to take notes comparing the vain churchgoer and the moping young bride. Write how they are alike where the circles overlap. Write how they are different where the circles are separate.

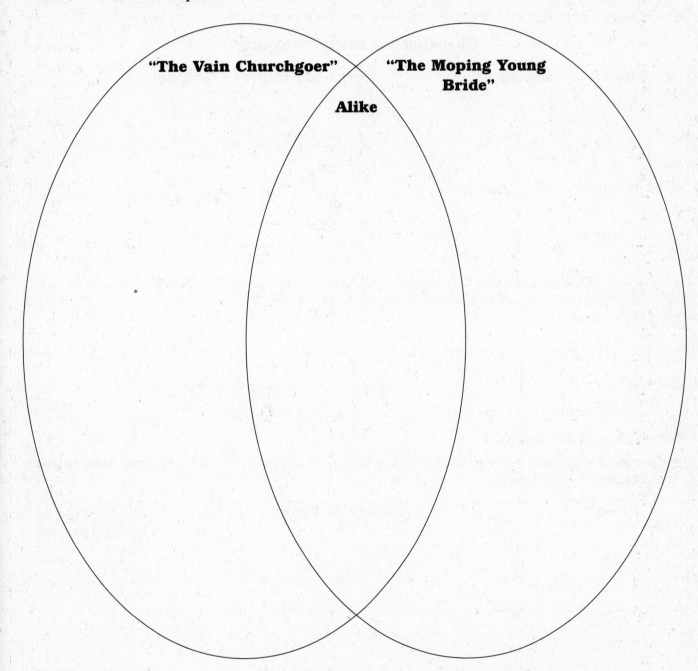

"The Vain Churchgoer"

"The Moping Young Bride"

Alike

On a separate page, use the details about the churchgoer and the bride to write an essay comparing the two.

Name _____ Date _____

"**To a Mouse**" and "**To a Louse**" by Robert Burns
"**Woo'd and Married and A'**" by Joanna Baillie

Support for Extend Your Learning

Listening and Speaking

On your photocopy of each poem, mark pronunciations and places where you can change your emphasis, tone, and reading rate, and points where you can show gestures and facial expressions. Then, use this checklist as you rehearse to improve your reading.

Checklist for Dialect Reading

Techniques	Rating	How I can improve technique
Pronunciation		
Raise or lower voice for stress		
Change tone		
Slow down or speed up rate of reading		
Hand gestures and facial expressions		

Research and Technology

Use the following chart to record information about the visuals you locate for your **multimedia presentation** on Scotland.

Visual	Source of Visual	Land (L) or History (H)

"To a Mouse" and **"To a Louse"** by Robert Burns
"Woo'd and Married and A'" by Joanna Baillie
Enrichment: Social Studies

   Both Robert Burns and Joanna Baillie chose to write their poetry in Scottish dialect in order to celebrate Scotland's culture. Today, people continue to celebrate their cultures through language, as well as through food, clothing, and music. Contemporary American culture is often described as a salad bowl, or a mix of many different cultures.

DIRECTIONS: *Use the following table to compare the culture of Burns and Baillie with that of one of the cultures that makes up the salad bowl of America. Choose a culture with which you are familiar. At the top of the second column, identify the American culture that you chose. Complete the column for the culture you have chosen based on your personal experience or knowledge, and study the poems by Burns and Baillie to find out more about Scottish culture. You may want to locate additional information by doing research.*

Culture	1. Burns's and Baille's Scotland	2.
Language		
Clothing		
Music		
Food		

"To a Mouse" and **"To a Louse"** by Robert Burns
"Woo'd and Married and A'" by Joanna Baillie
Selection Test A

Critical Reading *Identify the letter of the choice that best answers the question.*

____ 1. How is the mouse's home destroyed in "To a Mouse"?
   A. Snow and sleet destroy it.
   B. The speaker's plow destroys it.
   C. The speaker accidentally steps on it.
   D. A flood washes it away.

____ 2. Which line from "To a Mouse" contains dialect?
   A. "Thou thought to dwell"
   B. "In proving foresight may be vain"
   C. "That wee bit heap o' leaves an' stibble"
   D. "I'm truly sorry man's dominion"

____ 3. Which is the best translation of this line of dialect from "To a Mouse"?
   Thy wee bit housie, too, in ruin!
   A. Your small house is also destroyed!
   B. Your wee head is hurt, too!
   C. You should run from your house!
   D. You ruin your own house, too!

____ 4. What feelings does the speaker have for the mouse in "To a Mouse"?
   A. admiration
   B. anger
   C. disgust
   D. sympathy

____ 5. What is the main idea of "To a Louse"?
   A. Lice are very common on people of the upper class.
   B. It would do us all good if we could see ourselves as others do.
   C. Usually, only people of the lower class have lice.
   D. We should make more effort to hide our faults from others.

____ 6. Which line from "To a Louse" contains dialect?
   A. "Your impudence protects you."
   B. "Ha! whare ye gaun, ye crowlin' ferlie!"
   C. "On some poor body."
   D. "Your thick plantations."

_____ 7. Which is the best translation of this line from "To a Louse"?

      O, Jenny, dinna toss your head,
      An' set your beauties a' abroad!

    A. Oh, Jenny, don't toss your head or the lice will bite everyone!

    B. Oh, Jenny, don't toss your head at dinner or lice will go in the bread!

    C. Oh, Jenny, don't lose your head just because you are so beautiful!

    D. Oh, Jenny, don't toss your head and scatter the lice all over!

_____ 8. Why is the bride crying in "Woo'd and Married and A'"?

    A. She does not want to be married.

    B. Her parents do not approve of the wedding.

    C. She does not have beautiful clothes.

    D. Her husband is poor and her life will be hard.

_____ 9. Which is the best translation of this line of dialect from "Woo'd and Married and A'"?

      I think ye are very weel aff
      To be woo'd and married at a'.

    A. I think you are very well off to be courted and married and all.

    B. I think you would be better off living alone in the woods.

    C. I think you are very wise to reject the man's offer of marriage.

    D. I think you would be better off if you ran off and got married.

_____ 10. What does the bride learn in "Woo'd and Married and A'"?

    A. Love is not necessary for a happy marriage.

    B. Marrying a man who loves her is enough.

    C. Having a house of her own is the most important thing in life.

    D. If she and her husband work hard, they will eventually be rich.

Vocabulary and Grammar

_____ 11. Which sentence uses a vocabulary word *incorrectly*?

    A. The louse had the *discretion* to boldly climb to the peak of the hat.

    B. The mouse's *dominion* stretched as far as the curls.

    C. His attitude *inconstantly* changed from love to anger.

    D. The *winsome* young woman stole the boy's heart.

_____ **12.** What is the interjection in this line from "To a Louse"?

    My sooth! right bauld ye set your nose out,

    A. "right bauld"

    B. "ye set your nose"

    C. "out"

    D. "My sooth!"

Essay

13. In an essay, compare the attitudes shown by the bride and her mother in "Woo'd and Married and A.'" How are they either alike or different? Give at least two examples from the poem to support your comparison.

14. Dialect is a strong element in each of the three poems. Choose one of the poems and discuss its use of dialect. Consider these questions: How does dialect contribute to your enjoyment of the poem? Does it make the poem more difficult? Does it make the poem more interesting? Would the poem be more or less effective if dialect were not used? Explain your answers, using examples from the poem.

"To a Mouse" and **"To a Louse"** by Robert Burns
"Woo'd and Married and A'" by Joanna Baillie
Selection Test B

Critical Reading *Identify the letter of the choice that best completes the statement or answers the question.*

____ 1. Which lines from "To a Mouse" contain an example of dialect?
  A. "I'm truly sorry man's dominion"
  B. "Has broken Nature's social union,"
  C. "Has cost thee mony a weary nibble!"
  D. "In proving foresight may be vain:"

____ 2. In "To a Mouse," the poet's attitude toward the mouse is chiefly one of _____.
  A. pity
  B. scorn
  C. respect
  D. disgust

____ 3. The central objects of the poet's scorn in "To a Louse" are
  A. religion and ritual.
  B. vanity and conceit.
  C. gossip and slander.
  D. fashion and finery.

____ 4. Which line from "To a Louse" contains an example of dialect?
  A. "and seek your dinner / On some poor body."
  B. "dare unsettle / Your thick plantations."
  C. "a blunder free us / And foolish notion. . . ."
  D. "Detested, shunned by saunt an' sinner . . ."

____ 5. Which statement best translates the passage?
  How dare ye set your fit upon her, / Sae fine a lady? / Gae somewhere else, and seek your dinner / On some poor body. / Swith! in some beggar's haffet squattle;

  A. This lady must have found you in a beggar's house.
  B. You should live on a beggar, not a wealthy lady.
  C. You attack wealthy and poor people both.
  D. You should not depend on others for your dinner.

____ 6. Which strategy would be most helpful in translating the line?
  What airs in dress an' gait wad lea's us,
  And ev'n devotion!

  A. speaking words aloud, listening for similarities to standard English
  B. reading the footnote
  C. noting that apostrophes signal that a letter has been omitted
  D. looking for similarities between dialect words and standard English words

____ 7. What is the bride's principal concern in the poem "Woo'd and Married and A'"?
    A. She is not in love with her bridegroom.
    B. She has nothing beautiful to wear.
    C. The bridegroom is too old for her.
    D. She fears a life of poverty and drudgery.

____ 8. Which statement best describes what the bride learns in "Woo'd and Married and A'"?
    A. Marrying Johnny, who loves her, is enough.
    B. She and Johnny will have wealth eventually.
    C. Most people are poor when they first get married.
    D. She is not really too young to be married.

____ 9. Which words best describe the character of the bridegroom in "Woo'd and Married and A'"?
    A. clever and wise
    B. foolish and poor
    C. wealthy and wise
    D. irresponsible and clever

____ 10. Judging by the dialect in "Woo'd and Married and A'," what can you conclude about the characters?
    A. They are poor English workers.
    B. They are poor but well educated.
    C. They are poorly educated Scots.
    D. They are well educated Scots.

____ 11. Which phrase best translates this line from "Woo'd and Married and A'"?
    Is na' she very weel aff . . .?

    A. Does he think she is very well off?
    B. Does he think she is foolish?
    C. Isn't she very foolish?
    D. Isn't she very well off?

Vocabulary and Grammar

____ 12. Which word is the closest in meaning to *dominion*?
    A. authority
    B. discipline
    C. nationality
    D. society

____ 13. Which word means the opposite of *impudence*?
    A. rudeness
    B. shamelessness
    C. happiness
    D. courtesy

___ **14.** Which phrase is the closest in meaning to *discretion*?
   A. bad judgment
   B. good judgment
   C. lack of purpose
   D. good manners

___ **15.** Which of the lines from "To a Mouse" contains an interjection?
   A. "Thy wee bit housie, too, in ruin!"
   B. "An' cozie here, beneath the blast, / Thou thought to dwell. . . ."
   C. "But, och! I backward cast my e'e. . . ."
   D. "An' lea'e us nought but grief an' pain, / For promised joy."

___ **16.** In which of the following sentences is the interjection correctly punctuated?
   A. The mouse, poor thing, is without a home!
   B. Oh, no the winter has arrived!
   C. Alas, that mouse is afraid!
   D. The winter will be cold I fear and the wind strong!

Essay

17. Joanna Baillie and Robert Burns lived at the same time and both came from Scotland, so they shared the same background and many of the same cultural experiences. Write an essay in which you compare "Woo'd and Married and A'" with "To a Mouse" and "To a Louse." Were these poems written for the same audience? Are the values expressed in the poems similar or different? Do the poets use similar or different techniques in their writing? Provide evidence from the poems to support your response.

18. Robert Burns wrote poetry that was popular in Scotland. When he died, thousands attended his funeral procession and he was named the national poet of Scotland. Write an essay in which you explain how "To a Mouse" and "To a Louse" would help Burns achieve such a reputation. How do you think the use of dialect contributed to his popularity? What would his countrypeople think of his themes and subject matter?

Study these words from the selections. Then, complete the activities that follow.

Word List A

aspire [uh SPYR] *v.* to have a great ambition or goal; desire strongly
   I hope my child will <u>aspire</u> to attend college.

bound [BOWND] *v.* confined by limits; tied
   The medic <u>bound</u> the soldier's broken arm with a bandage.

mead [MEED] *n.* a meadow
   We had our picnic on the <u>mead</u> behind our house.

mild [MYLD] *adj.* gentle or kind in behavior; pleasant
   Janet is such a <u>mild</u> person that she smiles at everyone she meets.

rejoice [rih JOYS] *v.* celebrate
   My friends and I will <u>rejoice</u> when we graduate from high school.

seize [SEEZ] *v.* grab; take possession of something forcefully
   Li did not make her loan payments, so the bank will soon <u>seize</u> her car.

struggling [STRUG ling] *v.* striving; to make a strenuous effort
   Martha is <u>struggling</u> to learn how to swim.

wept [WEPT] *v.* shed tears; cried
   We <u>wept</u> during the sad part of the movie.

Word List B

distant [DIS tent] *adj.* separate or apart in space; far away
   The settler traveled to the <u>distant</u> town by train.

dread [DRED] *adj.* causing terror or fear
   The monster inspired a <u>dread</u> awe among the children.

grasp [GRASP] *n.* the act of firmly holding; an embrace
   It is difficult to <u>grasp</u> something that is slippery.

immortal [im MORT uhl] *adj.* living forever; not subject to death
   No living creature is <u>immortal</u> because all organisms must eventually die.

meek [MEEK] *adj.* easily imposed on; submissive
   Tara's <u>meek</u> response indicated that she was not sure of her answer.

sinews [SIN yooz] *n.* tendons or other strong connecting tissues
   The bodybuilder's <u>sinews</u> stood out strongly when he flexed his muscles.

striving [STRYV ing] *v.* to contend; to struggle forcefully
   Ambitious people are always <u>striving</u> to achieve great things.

sulk [SUHLK] *v.* to be silently withdrawn
   When her mother refused to give her more ice cream, Jamie began to <u>sulk</u>.

Name _____ Date _____

Selected Poetry of William Blake
Vocabulary Warm-up Exercises

Exercise A *Fill in each blank below using the appropriate word from Word List A.*

The weather was [1] _____ and sunny. There was a gentle breeze blowing

over the waving grass of the [2] _____ and onto the hills beyond it. We

were [3] _____ to carry our camping equipment into the meadow. The

equipment was [4] _____ with heavy rope so that it would stay in place in

our packs. The rope binding made it easier to [5] _____ and carry the

heavy packs. When we reached the meadow, Jane [6] _____ from the

pain that her blisters caused her. Our hope was to camp in the meadow for three days,

but a change in the weather suddenly brought flood conditions that forced us to change

our minds. We had to climb into the hills to reach safety. I knew we would both

[7] _____ when we escaped the dangerously rising water. For our next

trip, we will [8] _____ to complete a much easier activity.

Exercise B *Revise each of the following statements so that it makes sense. Be sure to include the underlined vocabulary words in your revised sentences.*

1. An <u>immortal</u> character in a story is likely to die before the end.

   _____

2. A <u>meek</u> person is very outgoing.

   _____

3. If something is <u>distant</u>, it is nearby.

   _____

4. Injured <u>sinews</u> would not affect an athlete's ability to do gymnastics.

   _____

5. If you <u>grasp</u> a ball, it will bounce away.

   _____

6. If you <u>sulk</u> about something, it means that you are very happy about it.

   _____

7. One example of a <u>dread</u> noise is a bird's chirping.

   _____

8. A person lying on his sofa all day is clearly <u>striving</u> to achieve his fitness goals.

   _____

Name _____ Date _____

Selected Poetry of William Blake
Reading Warm-up A

Read the following passage. Pay special attention to the underlined words. Then, read it again, and complete the activities. Use a separate sheet of paper for your written answers.

Jeff believes that people should have the ability to nurture any special abilities that they have. He thinks people should <u>seize</u> opportunities to explore their potential. If people want to <u>aspire</u> to achieve their creative goals, Jeff is willing to help them.

To help those people who are <u>struggling</u> with difficulty to survive as artists on their own, Jeff used part of his vast fortune to open a school that supports them in their goals. Many of the first artists to be admitted to this school were so grateful that they <u>wept</u> with tears of joy. They could <u>rejoice</u> because they would no longer have to strive on their own and face the difficulties of poverty and loneliness.

Jeff's school focuses on providing these artists with an education that would aid them in the creative process. To do this, the school provides the artists with housing. Even though the living quarters are not fancy, the artists decorate them and make each one unique. In exchange for their education and housing, the artists are simply required to present Jeff with an example of their best work at the end of their stay.

The artists are free to create what they choose, and they produce many different pieces of art. One woman painted a landscape scene that pictured a <u>mead</u>, wildflowers, and a clear blue sky. This <u>mild</u> and gentle image of a peaceful meadow is contrasted by an abstract sculpture made of metal strips that are <u>bound</u> by heavy chains.

Jeff is satisfied that he is doing his part to help artists and encourage artistic expression in his community. He hopes that other people who are more fortunate will also find a cause they would be willing to support in order to improve society.

1. Underline the words that tell what people should <u>seize</u>. What is a word that means about the same as *seize*?

2. Underline the phrase that tells what some people want to <u>aspire</u> to. What is something you *aspire* to?

3. Circle the words that hint at what <u>struggling</u> means. Use *struggling* in a sentence.

4. Circle that word that hints at what <u>wept</u> means. What is a happy occasion at which you have seen someone who *wept* for joy?

5. Circle the word in a nearby sentence that indicates what <u>rejoice</u> means. What is an example of something about which someone might *rejoice*?

6. Underline the words that tell what a <u>mead</u> is. What is something children might do in a *mead*?

7. Circle the word that means about the same as <u>mild</u>. What is a word that means the opposite of *mild*?

8. Underline the phrase that tells by what the metal strips of the sculpture were <u>bound</u>. Tell what *bound* means.

Name _____ Date _____

Selected Poetry of William Blake
Reading Warm-up B

Read the following passage. Pay special attention to the underlined words. Then, read it again, and complete the activities. Use a separate sheet of paper for your written answers.

William Blake was a poet who lived during the late-eighteenth to early-nineteenth centuries. He was constantly <u>striving</u> to combine art with poetry, and the result that he achieved is a delight to read and to view.

It did not take Blake's parents long to <u>grasp</u> that he had an artistic ability that needed to be developed, so they sent him to study art. Blake learned engraving and practiced it for many years. Blake combined his interests in poetry and engraving in books that he created.

Blake was not <u>meek</u> or shy when it came to publishing his work. He published most of the work that he created himself; he developed a special method and invention that allowed him to design and print illustrations and words at the same time. The results are considered startling and original, as the art weaves in and about the words that are on the printed page. The process took a great deal of muscle work, however, and Blake must have developed strong <u>sinews</u> as a result.

While Blake published frequently and was associated with many famous intellectuals of his day, he lived for most of his life in poverty, a <u>dread</u> condition of desperation. The invention he used to engrave and print words at the same time was very expensive.

Fame was also a <u>distant</u> dream. During his life, Blake's poetry was not popular. However, Blake did not <u>sulk</u> about this problem; instead of worrying and pouting about it, he continued to follow his interests. Today, people take Blake's work very seriously, and he is regarded as one of the greatest poets and engravers of his time. His work is now considered by many to be <u>immortal</u> because it will never die as long as people study it and enjoy it.

1. Underline the phrase that tells what Blake was <u>striving</u> to achieve. What is a synonym for **striving**?

2. Underline the phrase that tells what Blake's parents came to <u>grasp</u> about him. Tell what **grasp** means in this particular sentence.

3. Circle the word that means about the same as <u>meek</u>. How does a **meek** person act?

4. Underline the words that tell why Blake probably developed strong <u>sinews</u>. What might happen if a swimmer injured the **sinews** in her arms?

5. Circle the word that tells what <u>dread</u> condition Blake lived in. What is a word that means about the same as **dread** and could be used in this sentence without changing its meaning?

6. Underline the sentence that explains why fame was a <u>distant</u> dream for Blake. Use **distant** in a sentence.

7. Circle the words that tell what <u>sulk</u> means. How do people look when they **sulk**?

8. Circle the words that tell what <u>immortal</u> means. Give an example of an **immortal** character in literature.

"The Lamb," "The Tyger," "The Chimney Sweeper," and **"Infant Sorrow"** by William Blake
Literary Analysis: Symbols

Poets sometimes create their own **symbols,** but frequently they draw on symbols that should be familiar to everyone. Such symbols come from religious texts such as the Bible, as well as from stories that are common throughout a culture, such as a fairy tale or a beloved book. The more associations the reader can make with a given symbol in a poem, the richer the appreciation of the poem.

DIRECTIONS: *Following are some of the symbols in Blake's poetry. For each symbol, give one symbolic meaning and identify the source of the symbolic connection.*

1. lamb

   Meaning: _____

   Source: _____

2. fire

   Meaning: _____

   Source: _____

3. swaddling bands

   Meaning: _____

   Source: _____

4. child

   Meaning: _____

   Source: _____

5. anvil

   Meaning: _____

   Source: _____

6. angel

   Meaning: _____

   Source: _____

Name _____ Date _____

Reading Strategy: Use Visuals as a Key to Meaning

When you read any form of literature that has accompanying illustrations, you can **use the visuals as a key to meaning** by studying the details of the illustrations and thinking about how they relate to the information provided by the author's words. Look at visuals and consider how they support or add to information about characters or events. Blake's vivid illustrations accompany both "The Lamb" and "The Tyger." A late-nineteenth-century engraving, accompanies the poems "The Chimney Sweeper" and "Infant Sorrow" in your textbook. By looking closely at the details of these illustrations you can gather clues about Blake's meaning and about the characters, ideas, or situations described in the poems.

DIRECTIONS: *Use the graphic organizer below to help you use the visuals as a key to Blake's meaning. Study the illustrations as you read each poem. Gather and chart clues that support or add to information in the poems. The first one has been done for you.*

Poem	What the Illustrations Add to the Meaning
"The Lamb"	**1.** One of the lambs in the illustration is eating from the boy's hand, supporting the description of the lamb as meek and docile.
"The Tyger"	**2.**
"The Chimney Sweeper"	**3.**
"Infant Sorrow"	**4.**

29

"The Lamb," "The Tyger," "The Chimney Sweeper," and **"Infant Sorrow"** by William Blake
Vocabulary Builder

Using the Root *-spir-*

A. DIRECTIONS: *Each of the following sentences includes an italicized word that contains the word root -spir-, which means "breath" or "life." Fill in each blank with a word or phrase to complete the sentence and reveal the meaning of the italicized word.*

1. If the young woman is *spirited*, she _____.

2. If he was *dispirited* by the bad news, he _____.

3. If we waited to see what would *transpire*, we _____.

4. If the council member's term *expired*, it _____.

5. If the poem *inspires* the reader, it _____.

Using the Word List

vales	symmetry	aspire

B. DIRECTIONS: *Match each word in the left column with its definition in the right column. Write the letter of the definition on the line next to the word it defines.*

___ 1. vales   A. balance of forms

___ 2. symmetry   B. hollows

___ 3. aspire   C. seek after

C. DIRECTIONS: *Complete each sentence by filling in the blank with one of the words from the word bank.*

1. The rolling hills and grassy _____ were the landscape of his earliest memories.

2. Early on he learned to appreciate the veins of leaves, the wings of butterflies—in short, all of nature's _____.

3. With all of these influences it was only natural that he would _____ to become a nature photographer.

"The Lamb," "The Tyger," "The Chimney Sweeper," and **"Infant Sorrow"** by William Blake
Grammar and Style: Commonly Confused Words: *Rise* and *Raise*

The forms of the irregular verb *rise*, which means "to get up," are often confused with those of the regular verb *raise*, which means "to lift or elevate." The forms of the verb *rise* are *rise, rose, had risen*. The forms of the verb *raise* are *raise, raised, had raised*. Note the following examples:

Rise
Present: We *rise* early in the morning.
Past: I *rose* before the sun came up.
Past Participle: We *had risen* early in order to catch the first train.

Raise
Present: He *raises* the canoe onto the truck's roof.
Past: I *raised* the bookshelf up a few inches.
Past Participle: She *had raised* both of the ladders onto the platform.

A. PRACTICE: *Underline the forms of the verb* rise *or* raise *in each of the following lines. In the blank, identify whether the verb is a form of* rise *or* raise *and identify the form in which it appears. The first one is done for you.*

1. The King <u>rose</u> one morning and decided he wanted to conquer the world.
   rise: past tense
   _____

2. One night the King had a dream that the sun had risen in the west.
   _____
   _____

3. He called his ministers into council and raised the issue of conquest.
   _____
   _____

4. He took this dream as a bad omen and doubts rose in his mind.
   _____
   _____

B. Writing Application: *Rewrite each sentence using the verb tense of* rise *or* raise *indicated in parentheses.*

1. The sun had risen over the far horizon. (present)
   _____
   _____

2. We rise and gather up our camp equipment. (past)
   _____
   _____

3. Abigail and John raised the kayak onto the roof of the car. (past participle)
   _____
   _____

4. I watch as morning mist rises from the nearby river. (past)
   _____
   _____

"The Lamb," "The Tyger," "The Chimney Sweeper," and **Infant Sorrow** by William Blake
Support for Writing

Use the chart below to take notes for your literary analysis. First, write your thesis statement in the center circle. Then, find details in the two poems to support your comparison and the poems' connection to Blake's life.

Details from "The Tyger"

Details from "The Lamb"

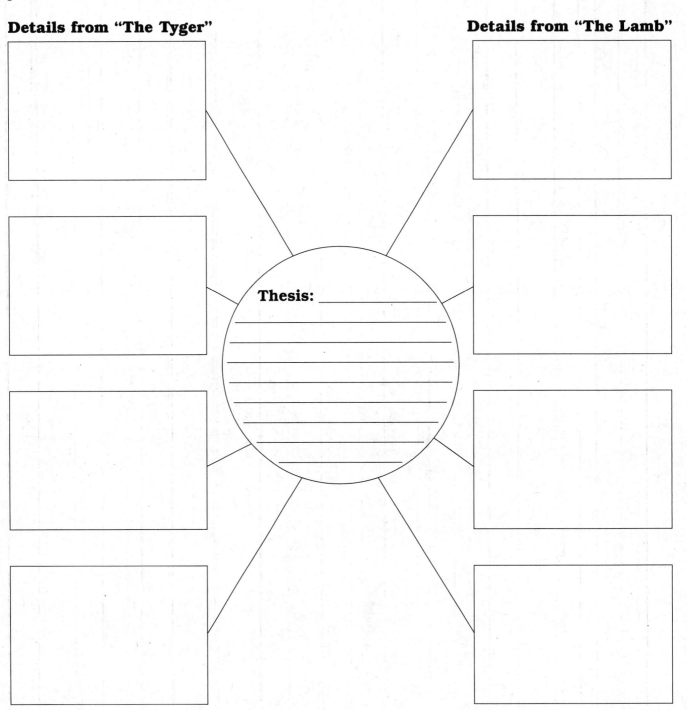

Thesis: _____

On a separate page, use the information in your chart to write your comparative literary analysis.

"The Lamb," "The Tyger," "The Chimney Sweeper," and **"Infant Sorrow"** by William Blake
Support for Extend Your Learning

Listening and Speaking

Poets evoke mood by using words and images. Write the words, images, and mood from the poems you choose for your **musical reading.**

Words and Images	Mood Evoked

Research and Technology

Use the following organizer to help you identify a possible symbol for your **advertisement.** First, write your idea for a product in the center circle. Then, write ideas or things that you associate with it. One of these ideas might be your symbol.

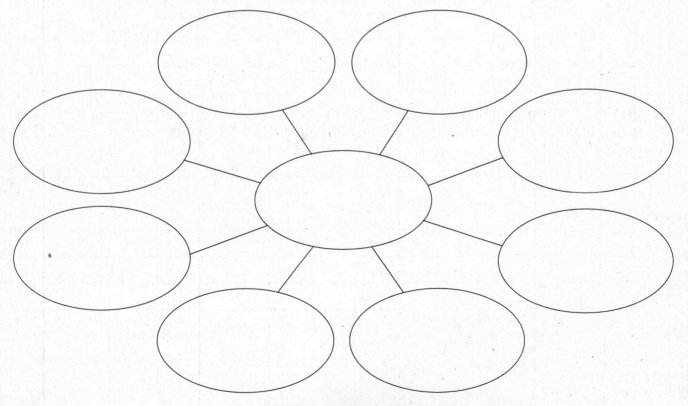

Name _____ Date _____

"The Lamb," "The Tyger," "The Chimney Sweeper," and **"Infant Sorrow"** by William Blake
Enrichment: Fine Art

   William Blake created unique and striking illustrations to accompany many of his poems. These illustrations, which help convey the meaning and emotions of the poems, were frequently as visionary as the poems themselves.

DIRECTIONS: *Answer the following questions on the lines provided.*

1. Look at Blake's illustrated versions of "The Lamb" and "The Tyger" in your textbook. What characteristics do the images share with the poems they accompany? How do the styles, colors, and images in the illustrations relate to the content of each poem?

   _____

   _____

   _____

   _____

   _____

2. Blake's works explore the world of emotions and ideas using a unique system of symbols. "The Lamb" and "The Tyger" explore innocence and power. Compare and contrast the illustrations that accompany these poems. How are they different? How are they similar?

   _____

   _____

   _____

   _____

   _____

3. Blake's artistic accomplishments were neglected and ignored in his lifetime, but they anticipated many of the goals of the Romantic movement. How are his illustrations typical of Romanticism?

   _____

   _____

   _____

   _____

   _____

Name _____ Date _____

"The Lamb," "The Tyger," "The Chimney Sweeper,"
and **"Infant Sorrow"** by William Blake
Selection Test A

Critical Reading *Identify the letter of the choice that best answers the question.*

____ 1. Read the first few lines of "The Lamb":

   Little Lamb who made thee
   Dost thou know who made thee

   What question does the speaker ask the lamb?
   A. Why do you appear so peaceful?
   B. Who made you and gave you life?
   C. Where is your shepherd?
   D. Who is called by your name?

____ 2. What is the main idea of "The Lamb"?
   A. God is kind.
   B. The earth is beautiful.
   C. Life is a mystery.
   D. The universe is large.

____ 3. What is one idea that "The Lamb" symbolizes?
   A. the Creator
   B. the common person
   C. country life
   D. generosity

____ 4. To what is Blake referring in the italicized words in these lines from "The Tyger"?
   Tyger Tyger, burning bright, / In the *forests of the night* . . .
   A. the dangers of other animals
   B. the difficulties of living
   C. the darkness of the country
   D. nightmares and bad dreams

____ 5. What does the tiger symbolize in "The Tyger"?
   A. peace
   B. anger
   C. power
   D. love

___ 6. Which word best describes Blake's drawings used to illustrate "The Lamb" and "The Tyger"?

    A. childlike

    B. modern

    C. colorless

    D. sophisticated

___ 7. Why is little Tom Dacre crying in "The Chimney Sweeper"?

    A. His mother abandoned him.

    B. He was sold to a chimney sweep.

    C. He broke his arm while sweeping.

    D. His head was shaved.

___ 8. Why was Tom Dacre happy and warm on the cold morning in "The Chimney Sweep"?

    A. He was relieved to wake up and find that his friends were not dead.

    B. He knew he would not have to be a chimney sweep all his life.

    C. He believed that if he were a good boy, God would be his father.

    D. He knew the soot would not blacken his white hair any longer.

___ 9. How does the father react to the child's birth in "Infant Sorrow"?

    A. He cries.

    B. He leaves.

    C. He groans.

    D. He leaps for joy.

Vocabulary and Grammar

___ 10. Which of the following is the best synonym for *vales* in these lines from "The Lamb"?

    By the stream & o'er the mead . . .
    Making all the *vales* rejoice!

    A. sorrow

    B. laughter

    C. valleys

    D. lambs

___ 11. Which sentence uses a vocabulary word *incorrectly*?

    A. Most homes had a *symmetry* sticking up from the roof.

    B. A heavy fog drifted up the *vale*.

    C. He *aspires* to do something other than sweep chimneys.

    D. Sheep were gathered together in the steep-sided *vale*.

_____ **12.** Which sentence uses a form of *rise* or *raise* incorrectly?

    A. The little chimney sweep *rose* early.

    B. He *rises* a question about his hair.

    C. He *raised* his broom and greeted the day.

    D. He climbs to the roof and *raises* his hand to wave.

Essay

13. In "The Tyger," the speaker asks, "Did he who made the Lamb make thee?" What does this line mean, and what is the best answer to the question? In an essay, connect this question's meaning to Blake's poem "The Lamb."

14. What attitude does Blake express toward chimney sweepers in his poem "The Chimney Sweeper"? Develop your answers in an essay. Give evidence from the poem to support your response.

"The Lamb," "The Tyger," "The Chimney Sweeper,"
and **"Infant Sorrow"** by William Blake
Selection Test B

Critical Reading *Identify the letter of the choice that best completes the statement or answers the question.*

____ 1. Which is an abstract idea symbolized by the lamb in Blake's poem "The Lamb"?
    A. knowledge
    B. reason
    C. innocence
    D. ecstasy

____ 2. A central idea of "The Lamb" is the
    A. beauty of the earth.
    B. excitement of experience.
    C. vastness of the universe.
    D. kindness of the creator.

____ 3. Whom does Blake refer to as "He" in "The Lamb"?
    A. the Creator
    B. the shepherd
    C. the lamb
    D. the child

____ 4. Which word best describes the mood of the illustration accompanying "The Lamb"?
    A. happy
    B. gloomy
    C. agitated
    D. serene

____ 5. A central image of "The Tyger" is
    A. power.
    B. death.
    C. guilt.
    D. peace.

____ 6. The images in Blake's illustrated versions of "The Lamb" and "The Tyger" can be best described as
    A. strictly classical in form.
    B. swirling through the words.
    C. sophisticated and refined.
    D. irrelevant to the poems themselves.

____ 7. Who is describing the action in "Infant Sorrow"?
    A. a mother
    B. a father
    C. a newborn infant
    D. an omniscient narrator

____ 8. What might the "swaddling bands" described in "Infant Sorrow" represent?
A. poverty
B. luxury
C. confinement
D. protection

____ 9. In "The Chimney Sweeper" the "coffins of black" are meant to be symbols for _____.
A. work
B. courage
C. youth
D. death

____ 10. In Blake's poem "The Chimney Sweeper," the "green plain" and "clouds" most clearly suggest
A. the roofs of houses.
B. the sky.
C. heaven or paradise.
D. the countryside.

____ 11. Which word best describes the attitude of Tom Dacre in "The Chimney Sweeper"?
A. optimistic
B. despairing
C. happy
D. fearful

____ 12. Which best describes using visuals as a key to meaning?
A. studying the use of descriptive language in a piece of writing
B. using illustrations to help understand accompanying text
C. charting details found in a piece of writing
D. analyzing and interpreting the symbols in a piece of writing

Vocabulary and Grammar

____ 13. Which word is the closest in meaning to *aspire*?
A. breath
B. descend
C. strive
D. observe

____ 14. Which phrase is the closest in meaning to *sinews*?
A. ropes and pulleys
B. mechanical power
C. muscular power
D. chemical power

____ 15. Which sentence contains an incorrect usage of the verb *rise* or *raise*?
A. We rose late and went to the tourist bureau.
B. Banners had been risen along the sides of the boulevard.
C. As we walked, I raised the issue of money.
D. Jim responded that we'd raise the cash to get home.

Unit 4 Resources: Rebels and Dreamers
39

_____ **16.** Which sentence uses the verb *rise* in its past tense form?
   A. The president announced that he would raise taxes.
   B. The people raised an uproar of protest.
   C. Public discontent rose to unprecedented levels.
   D. When taxes rise, so do tempers.

Essay

17. Blake was ignored in his own time and only came to be appreciated for his creativity over a century after his death. One twentieth-century critic has said that Blake was ignored in his own time because of the complexity of his vision. This critic has said that Blake's thinking and poetry frequently combine the "opposite sides of [the same] argument." Write an essay in which you relate the critic's statement to Blake's poems "The Lamb" and "The Tyger." What are the "opposite sides" that Blake expresses or describes in these two poems? What symbols does he use to describe these oppositions? Include evidence from the poems to support your points.

18. William Blake uses a wide range of simple and sophisticated symbols in "The Lamb," "The Tyger," "The Chimney Sweeper," and "Infant Sorrow." Write an essay in which you interpret the symbols in any two of the four poems. How do the symbols Blake uses in the two poems relate to the meaning of the poems? Why might he have chosen the symbols? Support your points with details from the poems.

Name _____ Date _____

Elizabeth McCracken Introduces "Introduction" to *Frankenstein* by Mary Shelley

DIRECTIONS: *Use the space provided to answer the questions.*

1. What was McCracken's recurring nightmare when she was a child?

_____

_____

_____

_____

2. A. What does McCracken mean by "the thrill of the terrifying"?

_____

_____

   B. Do you agree with McCracken that horror has a strange but widespread appeal to both children and adults? How would you explain this appeal?

_____

_____

_____

_____

3. According to McCracken, why did her dream about a Frankenstein monster impress her?

_____

_____

4. Why did McCracken become a fiction writer?

_____

_____

5. What questions about Mary Shelley's *Frankenstein* does McCracken's commentary raise in your mind at this point?

_____

_____

_____

_____

_____

_____

_____

Elizabeth McCracken
Listening and Viewing

Segment 1: Meet Elizabeth McCracken
- How does Elizabeth McCracken draw on her personal experiences to create characters for her stories?
- Why might real-life experiences be a good starting point for a story?

_____

_____

_____

_____

Segment 2: On Frankenstein
- Why is *Frankenstein* considered a "gothic novel"?
- Although *Frankenstein* was first published in 1818, people are still intrigued by this story today. What do you find timeless about the motivations of Dr. Frankenstein as described by McCracken?

_____

_____

_____

_____

Segment 3: The Writing Process
- How does Elizabeth McCracken "find" her plot?
- Why do you think it is important to be flexible when you develop plot?

_____

_____

_____

_____

Segment 4: The Rewards of Writing
- What advice does Elizabeth McCracken have for young writers?
- Do you agree or disagree with her advice?

_____

_____

_____

_____

Vocabulary Warm-up Word Lists

Study these words from the selection. Then, complete the activities that follow.

Word List A

acceded [ak SEED ed] *v.* yielded (to); agreed
We <u>acceded</u> to the judge's final decision.

adorns [uh DORNZ] *v.* gives beauty; decorates
A ribbon <u>adorns</u> each dress.

contrive [kuhn TRYV] *v.* plan; devise
A clown must <u>contrive</u> ways to entertain the children.

devout [duh VOWT] *adj.* sincere; earnest
Never missing a performance, Judy is a <u>devout</u> opera fan.

endeavor [en DEV uhr] *n.* a purposeful, industrious activity
Levi puts great energy into each and every <u>endeavor</u>.

furnish [FUR nish] *v.* supply; give
The company should <u>furnish</u> instructions on how to use the dishwasher.

incitement [in SYT muhnt] *n.* act of urging; encouragement
With the coach's <u>incitement</u>, the team let out a roar of determination.

successively [suk SES iv lee] *adv.* in proper order or sequence
For three years, Dorothy took classes <u>successively</u>.

Word List B

appendage [uh PEN dij] *n.* something added on
An elephant's trunk is a very important <u>appendage</u> for this giant animal.

comply [kuhm PLY] *v.* act in accordance with another's rules or wishes
Barton was forced to <u>comply</u> with the rules of the game.

bestow [be STOH] *v.* to present as a gift or an honor
Selena was asked to <u>bestow</u> an award on the winner of the competition.

illustrious [il LUS tree uhs] *adj.* well-known and very distinguished
The university hired an <u>illustrious</u> scholar to be its new president.

incessant [in SES uhnt] *adj.* continuing without interruption
The baby's <u>incessant</u> crying has given me a headache.

odious [OH dee uhs] *adj.* detestable; horrible
Roger's <u>odious</u> personality made his coworkers avoid him.

platitude [PLAT uh tood] *n.* statement lacking originality
Instead of thoughtful advice, Gina repeated a meaningless <u>platitude</u>.

relinquished [ruh LINK wisht] *v.* let go of; gave up on
Mrs. Adams <u>relinquished</u> the keys to her house when it was sold.

Name _____ Date _____

"Introduction to Frankenstein" by Mary Wollstonecraft Shelley
Vocabulary Warm-up Exercises

Exercise A *Fill in each blank below using the appropriate word from Word List A.*

Martha is a [1] _____ reader of decorating magazines; she reads every one that she can find. When it was time [2] _____ the classroom with holiday decorations, she immediately volunteered to do it. The other students [3] _____ to the teacher's decision to allow Martha to decorate because they were not interested in working after school. They knew about her passion for decorating, and they felt that she would [4] _____ to create a lovely and colorful decorating scheme for the room. Martha worked [5] _____ on this project, doing a little each day. At first, she was going to [6] _____ a scheme that used flowers of many shapes and colors. Instead, she used ribbons. Now that she is finished, a ribbon [7] _____ each of the windows in the room. Our [8] _____ of Martha's efforts encouraged her to use imagination to create a colorful and festive atmosphere for our winter celebration.

Exercise B *Decide whether each of the following statements is true or false. Circle T or F, and explain your answers.*

1. If something is <u>odious</u>, it is loved by many people.
   T / F _____

2. One example of an <u>appendage</u> is a tree trunk.
   T / F _____

3. Many cultures have holidays when people <u>bestow</u> gifts on one another.
   T / F _____

4. A <u>platitude</u> is an example of creative problem-solving.
   T / F _____

5. It is important to <u>comply</u> with the rules of the road when you are driving.
   T / F _____

6. Many professional athletes are <u>illustrious</u> figures in American culture.
   T / F _____

7. If you have <u>relinquished</u> control, you have given it up.
   T / F _____

8. A library is a place where there is <u>incessant</u> noise.
   T / F _____

Name _____ Date _____

"Introduction to Frankenstein" by Mary Wollstonecraft Shelley
Reading Warm-up A

Read the following passage. Pay special attention to the underlined words. Then, read it again, and complete the activities. Use a separate sheet of paper for your written answers.

Mary Wollstonecraft Shelley lived and wrote primarily during the nineteenth century. Her sincere and <u>devout</u> interest in literature arose out of the family and society in which she grew up. She was the only child of Mary Wollstonecraft, a famous feminist, and William Godwin, who was a philosopher and novelist.

From the time that she was born, Mary's father tried to <u>furnish</u> her with the belief that she would realize the great potential that her father believed she had. Thus, it was through her father's <u>incitement</u> and encouragement that Mary got an education and developed an understanding of literary and philosophical matters at a young age.

Mary wrote *Frankenstein, or The Modern Prometheus,* in 1818, when she was nineteen years old. She undertook this <u>endeavor</u> because her husband, the poet Percy Bysshe Shelley, suggested the task. During one rainy evening when Mary, Percy, and their friends had gathered at the fireside to read a book, Percy suggested that they should each <u>contrive</u> to write a horror story. The rest is history. Since that time, *Frankenstein* has been acclaimed as one of the most famous novels ever published. It <u>adorns</u> the bookshelves of countless literature fans all over the world, who admire it as an exceptional example of Gothic literature.

Nearly two hundred years later, this famous novel still inspires people to write plays and create films, and many scholars have <u>acceded</u> to the judgment it is a great work. The monster, which is the main character in the book, is a being that works <u>successively</u>, in a series of steps, to bring about the destruction of the young scientist who created him. Through her story, Mary warns against the dangers of relying heavily on scientific technology.

1. Circle the word that means about the same as <u>devout</u>. Use *devout* in a sentence.

2. Underline the words that tell what Mary's father tried to <u>furnish</u> for her. What is a synonym for *furnish*?

3. Circle the word that means about the same as <u>incitement</u>. Tell what *incitement* means.

4. Circle the word that means about the same as <u>endeavor</u>. What is an *endeavor* you might like to try some day?

5. Underline the phrase that tells why Mary and her friends decided to <u>contrive</u> to write horror stories. Tell what *contrive* means.

6. Underline the sentence that tells what judgment many scholars have <u>acceded</u> to. If a teacher *acceded* to his students' request for more time on an assignment, what would this mean?

7. Underline the phrase that tells what <u>successively</u> means. What is an example of something people do *successively*?

8. Underline the words that tell why *Frankenstein* <u>adorns</u> the bookshelves of Gothic literature fans. What is an example of something that often *adorns* the hair of little girls?

45

Name _____ Date _____

"Introduction to Frankenstein" by Mary Wollstonecraft Shelley
Reading Warm-up B

Read the following passage. Pay special attention to the underlined words. Then, read it again, and complete the activities. Use a separate sheet of paper for your written answers.

Gothic literature is a type of writing that was especially popular from about 1764 to 1840. Illustrious writers of this period included the well-known Mary Wollstonecraft Shelly, Lord Byron, Ann Radcliff, Emily Brontë, and Edgar Allan Poe. This literary movement did not focus on light matters. Instead, it focused on odious issues—including such detestable ones as ruin, decay, death, terror, and chaos.

The major themes of the Gothic novel, the dark side of human nature and the conflict between chaos and order, developed out of the time during which this literature was written. The period between 1750 and 1850 saw many changes in the ways that people saw their world. During this time, people valued logic. They relinquished the idea that emotion should be used to arrive at answers to questions. Moreover, many violent, political revolutions occurred that changed the way countries were governed and brought in new rules with which people had to comply; failing to follow these rules was not an option.

Terror and horror are two different but incessant and repetitive elements in Gothic writing. One Gothic writer described terror as growing out of suspense, like an appendage. Horror may arise out of a terrible event that affects an individual. The combination of these two elements works to bestow a feeling in readers that the characters in these novels lack a sense of balance because they are caught between the anticipation of a frightening event and the feeling of horror when the event actually occurs. Gothic writers, who loved to explore dark and supernatural themes, probably would not have agreed with the platitude that there is nothing to fear but fear itself. This common saying is completely opposite of the ideas about which these authors wrote.

1. Circle the word that tells what illustrious means. Use *illustrious* in a sentence.

2. Circle the word that tells what odious means. What is an example of something you find to be *odious*?

3. Underline the phrase that tells what people relinquished. Tell what *relinquished* means.

4. Circle the words that mean the opposite of comply. What is an example of a rule with which you must *comply*?

5. Circle the words that identify the incessant elements in Gothic literature. Use *incessant* in a sentence.

6. Underline the phrase that describes how terror might be like an appendage. What is an example of an *appendage* that a monkey can use to move through trees?

7. Underline the phrase that tells what horror and terror work to bestow. Tell what *bestow* means.

8. Circle the words in a nearby sentence that explain what a platitude is. What is an example of another *platitude*?

Name _____ Date _____

Introduction to Frankenstein by Mary Wollstonecraft Shelley
Literary Analysis: The Gothic Tradition

To the Romantics of the early nineteenth century, the **Gothic** elements of mystery, variety, richness, and primitive wildness suggested the natural, free, authentic aspects of life that they valued. The Gothic novel was characterized by mystery, chivalry, and horror. The Gothic tradition emphasized setting and plot more than character; often, an atmosphere of brooding and terror pervaded Gothic novels.

DIRECTIONS: *Answer the following questions about how Mary Shelley's Introduction to* Frankenstein *reflects the Gothic tradition.*

1. How might the Swiss setting in which Mary Wollstonecraft Shelley found herself in the summer of 1816 have inspired her to write a Gothic novel?

_____

_____

_____

_____

_____

_____

2. How did the stories that the writers read to amuse themselves help produce a frame of mind conducive to Gothic writing?

_____

_____

_____

_____

_____

3. How is the waking dream that Mary Wollstonecraft Shelley describes characteristic of the Gothic tradition?

_____

_____

_____

_____

_____

_____

_____

Name _____ Date _____

Introduction to Frankenstein by Mary Wollstonecraft Shelley
Reading Strategy: Predict

Making **predictions** about what will happen in a literary work keeps you involved in your reading. Use clues that the writer provides, along with what you learn about the characters and the pattern in which the work is organized. As you read, check your predictions and revise them as necessary.

DIRECTIONS: *In the lines following each excerpt, record what predictions you might make about Mary Shelly's novel Frankenstein.*

1. "'How I, then a young girl, came to think of, and to dilate upon, so very hideous an idea?'"

   _____

   _____

   _____

   _____

2. "I busied myself to think of a story—a story to rival those which had excited us to this task. One which would speak to the mysterious fears of our nature . . ."

   _____

   _____

   _____

   _____

3. ". . . various philosophical doctrines were discussed, and among others the nature of the principle of life and whether there was any probability of its ever being discovered and communicated."

   _____

   _____

   _____

   _____

4. "When I placed my head on my pillow, I did not sleep, nor could I be said to think. My imagination, unbidden, possessed and guided me, gifting the successive images that arose in my mind with a vividness far beyond the usual bounds of reverie."

   _____

   _____

   _____

   _____

Name _____   Date _____

Introduction to Frankenstein by Mary Wollstonecraft Shelley
Vocabulary Builder

Using Related Words: *Phantasm* and *Fantasy*

A. DIRECTIONS: *The word* phantasm *means "supernatural form or shape." It is related to the word* fantasy, *which means "a product of the imagination." Each italicized word in the following sentences is related to* phantasm *or* fantasy. *Replace each one with a synonymous word or phrase. Write the new word or phrase on the line following the sentence.*

1. To Dexter, the shadows looked like a parade of *fantastic* creatures. _____
2. When Sono opened her eyes, the *phantasm* was still there. _____
3. Angela liked to *fantasize* about quitting her job and moving to Alaska. _____
4. Scowling, Greg pronounced, "If you think you're entitled to another week of vacation, you're living in a *fantasy* land!" _____
5. The special effects in that movie were *phantasmagorical*! _____

Using the Word List

appendage	ungenial	acceded
platitude	phantasm	incitement

B. DIRECTIONS: *Fill in each blank with a word from the Word List to complete the sentence.*

1. Alex _____ to Lori's request not to reveal the plans for the surprise party.
2. Without much imagination, the speaker often used a _____ like "All's well that ends well."
3. The shimmering mist in Margo's office turned out to be steam from her teacup, not a _____.
4. The stock market always seems to crash during the _____ weather of October.
5. Tasha's encouragement was all the _____ Li needed to convince her to apply for the job.
6. Dan's pencil looked like an extra _____ growing above his ear.

Name _____   Date _____

Introduction to Frankenstein by Mary Wollstonecraft Shelley
Grammar and Style: Past Participial Phrases

A **past participle** is the form of a verb that is used along with a form of the verb "to have." In the following sentences, the past participle is italicized.

Juan wasn't hungry because he had already *eaten*.

I have *had* enough of your teasing!

A **past participial phrase** is a phrase that includes a past participle and acts as an adjective. The past participle and all the other words in the phrase work together to modify a noun or pronoun. In the following sentence, the past participial phrase is italicized.

Percy Bysshe Shelley wrote a ghost story *based on his childhood experiences*.

The past participial phrase "based on his childhood experiences" acts as an adjective for the noun "story."

A. PRACTICE: *Underline the past participial phrase in each sentence below, and circle the word it modifies.*

1. The illustrious poets also, annoyed by the platitude of prose, speedily relinquished their uncongenial task.

2. . . . he advanced to the couch of the blooming youths, cradled in healthy sleep.

3. Eternal sorrow sat upon his face as he bent down and kissed the foreheads of the boys, who from that hour withered like flowers snapped from the stalk.

4. He would hope that, left to itself, the slight spark of life which he had communicated would fade. . . .

B. Writing Application: *Rewrite each of these sentences, adding a past participial phrase that acts as an adjective to modify the italicized word.*

1. On Friday, all her best *students* were late to class.

   _____

2. The *plants* on Sara's windowsill withered and died.

   _____

3. The *house* was more dilapidated than haunted.

   _____

4. Several of the *stuffed animals* were in danger of falling to the floor.

   _____

5. *Samuel* did not listen to the train conductor's announcements and consequently missed his stop.

   _____

   _____

Name _____ Date _____

Support for Writing

Use the two charts below to take notes about your impressions of Dr. Frankenstein and his monster before reading the Introduction and after reading it.

Impressions: Dr. Frankenstein	
Before Reading	**After Reading**

Impressions: The Monster	
Before Reading	**After Reading**

On a separate page, use your charts to write an essay comparing your impressions of *Frankenstein* before you read the Introduction to your impressions after reading it.

Introduction to Frankenstein by Mary Wollstonecraft Shelley
Support for Extend Your Learning

Listening and Speaking

Use the chart below to plan your **radio play.** First, identify scenes in the story and the mood you want to create. Then, choose music that will enhance or complement the mood and events. List sound effects that will support the mood.

Scene	Mood	Music	Sound Effects

Research and Technology

In the boxes below, collect and organize information for your **science report.** First, write the steps in the process of cloning. Then, number the steps in the order in which they are taken.

Order	Steps in the process

Introduction to Frankenstein by Mary Wollstonecraft Shelley

Enrichment: Science

Mary Shelley published *Frankenstein* in 1818. Scientists in the 1800's, like the fictional Dr. Frankenstein, would have had access to some basic tools, such as microscopes and thermometers. However, nineteenth-century science was very different from modern science in some respects. For example, at the beginning of the nineteenth century, doctors still tried to cure disease by bleeding or applying leeches to the patient. The chart below contrasts nineteenth- and twentieth-century science.

Some scientific developments that occurred by or in the nineteenth century	Some of the scientific developments of the twentieth century
• scientific method	• X-rays
• discovery of atoms	• discovery of structure of the atom
• basic genetics	• discovery of DNA
• electricity	• computers
• magnets	• laser technology
• telescopes	• satellites
• microscopes	• rockets/space shuttle
• partial periodic table of elements	• nuclear physics

DIRECTIONS: *Refer to the chart as you answer the questions below.*

1. Name three activities of doctors or scientists today that would have been impossible in the nineteenth century.

   _____

   _____

   _____

2. If Shelley were alive today and wrote a new novel about the dangers of technology used for the wrong purposes, what might the plot be?

   _____

   _____

   _____

Introduction to Frankenstein by Mary Wollstonecraft Shelley
Selection Test A

Critical Reading *Identify the letter of the choice that best answers the question.*

____ 1. According to the Introduction, what were Shelley, her husband, Byron, and Polidori doing during the summer they wrote the ghost stories?
   A. They were living in different countries.
   B. They were on a summer vacation.
   C. They were mourning the loss of a friend.
   D. They were working in London.

____ 2. Which of Shelley's statements in the Introduction helps you predict that the friends will write ghost stories?
   A. "The Publishers of the Standard Novels, in selecting *Frankenstein* for one of their series, expressed a wish that I should furnish them with some account of the origin of the story."
   B. "But it proved a wet, ungenial summer, and incessant rain often confined us for days to the house. Some volumes of ghost stories . . . fell into our hands."
   C. "In the summer of 1816, we visited Switzerland, and became the neighbors of Lord Byron."
   D. "At first we spent our pleasant hours on the lake or wandering on its shores; and Lord Byron, who was writing the third canto of *Childe Harold*, was the only one among us who put his thoughts upon paper."

____ 3. What were Percy Bysshe Shelley and Lord Byron talking about that gave Mary Shelley the original idea for *Frankenstein*, according to the Introduction?
   A. how it can be proved that ghosts really exist
   B. if death can really be passed on with a kiss
   C. the consequences of peeping through a keyhole
   D. whether life could be created by people

____ 4. What was Shelley doing when she came up with the idea for *Frankenstein*, based on what she says in the Introduction?
   A. She was walking along a shore.
   B. She was listening to Byron.
   C. She was having a waking dream.
   D. She was thinking at her desk.

___ 5. To which type of modern writing does *Frankenstein* compare most closely?

   A. realistic novel

   B. science fiction

   C. romance novel

   D. historical novel

___ 6. What characteristic of the Romantic Movement did Shelley try to achieve in *Frankenstein,* according to the Introduction?

   A. to evoke intense, vivid feelings

   B. to explain mysterious events through logic

   C. to use everyday language and realistic settings

   D. to emphasize the power of reason

___ 7. According to the Introduction, who encouraged Mary Shelley to expand *Frankenstein* into a full-length novel?

   A. Lord Byron

   B. Dr. John Polidori

   C. Percy Bysshe Shelley

   D. the Publishers of the Standard Novels

___ 8. What characteristic do Gothic novels share with other literature in the Romantic tradition?

   A. They both express deep, personal emotions.

   B. They both always involve a plot about romantic love.

   C. Both place primary importance on evoking supernatural events.

   D. Both see the imagination as a creative force equal to that of nature.

___ 9. What element of the Gothic novel is apparent in Shelley's Introduction to *Frankenstein?*

   A. The story evokes dread and terror.

   B. The story is set in Switzerland.

   C. The story is written by a woman.

   D. The story teaches a moral.

Vocabulary and Grammar

___ 10. Which vocabulary word correctly completes the following sentence?

   Shelley described her introduction as a(n) _____ to her novel, *Frankenstein.*

   A. appendage

   B. platitude

   C. phantasm

   D. incitement

___ 11. Which sentence *incorrectly* uses a vocabulary word?

    A. Polidori's story was filled with *platitudes* and dull ideas, and he gave it up.

    B. The Shelleys *acceded* to Byron's suggestion to write stories of their own.

    C. The weather was *ungenial,* so they spent most of their time outdoors walking.

    D. Shelley's husband liked her story and gave her *incitements* to keep writing.

___ 12. Which sentence contains a past participial phrase?

    A. Byron was bored by the weather, and he suggested writing stories.

    B. Of the four, two were famous romantic poets.

    C. Shelley was the least experienced, but her story has been the most enduring.

    D. Shelley expanded her story, written on their vacation, into a novel.

Essay

13. Shelley describes the vision she had that formed the basis for *Frankenstein.* In an essay, describe elements of the Gothic tradition that you find in her vision. Give at least two examples.

14. Lord Byron suggested that the four people in the group each write a story. In an essay, tell how the stories came out. Who finished their stories? What kinds of problems did the writers have? Who was most successful? Why do you think this was the case? Use examples from the Introduction to support your response.

Introduction to Frankenstein by Mary Wollstonecraft Shelley
Selection Test B

Critical Reading *Identify the letter of the choice that best completes the statement or answers the question.*

____ 1. Which type of modern writing does *Frankenstein* resemble most closely?
   A. morality play
   B. familiar essay
   C. science fiction
   D. realistic novel

____ 2. What mental state does Mary Shelley say she was in when she thought of the idea for *Frankenstein*?
   A. deep slumber
   B. daytime reverie
   C. waking dream
   D. alert vigilance

____ 3. Which is a favorite aim of the Romantic poets that Mary Shelley also had in writing *Frankenstein*?
   A. to use the language of everyday life
   B. to find evidence of the divine in nature
   C. to depict the ways of the common people
   D. to evoke intense and vivid feelings

____ 4. Mary Shelley's statement that because her introduction will be confined to topics related to *Frankenstein* alone, she can "scarcely accuse [herself] of a personal intrusion" implies that
   A. she respects her readers' privacy.
   B. she likes to write about herself.
   C. she is modest.
   D. *Frankenstein* is based on her personal life.

____ 5. Which was a key element of the Gothic novel that Mary Shelley set out to employ in *Frankenstein*?
   A. the inexplicable
   B. the educational
   C. the conventional
   D. the philosophical

____ 6. Which details from Shelley's "Introduction to *Frankenstein*" would lead you to predict that she would write a successful ghost story?
   A. "I busied myself to think of a story. . . ."
   B. "Perhaps a corpse would be reanimated: galvanism."
   C. "I saw the pale student of unhallowed arts kneeling beside the thing he had put together."
   D. "The idea so possessed my mind, that a thrill of fear ran through me. . . ."

_____ 7. Shelley says her husband wrote "the most melodious verse that adorns our language." From this statement, what do you infer about Shelley's feelings for her husband?
A. She loves him.
B. She admires him.
C. She resents his work.
D. She likes to tease him.

_____ 8. Which statement of Shelley's helps you to predict that the situation might lead to writing ghost stories?
A. "In the summer of 1816, we visited Switzerland, and became the neighbors of Lord Byron."
B. "At first we spent our pleasant hours on the lake or wandering on its shores . . ."
C. "But it proved wet, ungenial summer, and incessant rain often confined us for days to the house. Some volumes of ghost stories, translated from the German into French, fell into our hands."
D. "These, as he brought them successfully to us, clothed in all light and harmony of poetry, seemed to stamp as divine the glories of heaven and earth, whose influences we partook with him."

_____ 9. Shelley writes that after listening to the conversation with Lord Byron about Dr. Darwin, she could not sleep and instead saw a terrifying vision. This suggests that
A. the conversation inspired her to think of the idea for her story.
B. she was frightened by the experiments of Dr. Darwin.
C. the poets were the first to think of the idea for *Frankenstein.*
D. Dr. Darwin's work was scarier than any ghost story.

_____ 10. The poets Percy Shelley and Lord Byron had trouble writing the ghost story assignment because they were "annoyed by the platitudes of prose." What prediction might you make about Mary Shelley's story from this statement?
A. She will write her story in poetry form.
B. She will use Percy Shelley and Lord Byron's ideas in her own story.
C. Her story, written in prose, will be the best story of all.
D. Her story will not be a ghost story after all.

_____ 11. Which element of the Gothic novel unites it with the Romantic tradition?
A. ordinary happenings
B. the supernatural
C. personal emotions
D. the religious

_____ 12. True to the Romantic culture of her time, Mary Shelley saw Frankenstein as the product of her
A. imagination.
B. rational mind.
C. education.
D. personal experience.

Vocabulary and Grammar

____ 13. In the passage, what does the word *appendage* mean?

> . . . as my account will only appear as an *appendage* to a former production . . .

A. introduction
B. epilogue
C. addition
D. revision

____ 14. In the sentence, what does the word *phantasm* suggest?

> I saw the hideous *phantasm* of a man stretched out . . .

A. The man is not really there.
B. The man is actually some kind of supernatural being.
C. The man has just died and is now a corpse.
D. Shelley only sees the man's shadow.

____ 15. Which italicized words are a past participial phrase?

A. These . . . *clothed in all the light and harmony* of poetry . . .
B. There was "The History of the Inconstant Lover," who, when he *thought to clasp* the bride . . .
C. found himself in the arms of the pale ghost of her whom *he had deserted.*
D. their incidents are as fresh in my mind as if I *had read them yesterday*

____ 16. Which italicized phrase is *not* a past participial phrase?

A. he advanced to the couch of the blooming youths, *cradled in healthy sleep.*
B. the boys, who from that hour withered like flowers *snapped upon the stalk.*
C. Shelley . . . commenced one *founded on the experiences of his early life.*
D. he . . . *was obliged to despatch her to the tomb of the Capulets.* . . .

Essay

17. One theme of *Frankenstein* is the potential danger of technology used for the wrong purposes. Think of a more contemporary work, such as a novel, short story, play, or movie, that explores this theme. Write an essay comparing *Frankenstein* with the contemporary work. How is each work connected to the ethical debates and controversies of its day? Be sure to briefly explain the plot of the contemporary work that you use.

18. The Gothic novel is considered a part and product of the Romantic Age. How can this be? Reconstruct the definition of Romanticism to find the answer. Remember that Romanticism is not easily defined, nor does it take only a single form. The Gothic novel has been referred to as sensational romance. Write an essay that explains how and why the Gothic novel should be a considered part and product of the Romantic Age.

Study these words from the selection. Then, complete the activities that follow.

Word List A

assist [uh SIST] *v.* to aid
　　We will <u>assist</u> our mother with the housework.

duties [DOO teez] *n.* obligations; an act required by custom, law, position, or religion
　　One of the secretary's <u>duties</u> is to keep a record of attendance at meetings.

gentle [JEN tuhl] *adj.* not harsh or severe; mild
　　The <u>gentle</u> breeze made us feel cool during the hot afternoon.

glimpses [GLIMP siz] *n.* quick, imcomplete views or looks
　　We could only catch <u>glimpses</u> of the movie stars as they entered the theatre.

inward [IN wuhrd] *adj.* located inside; inner
　　The hurricane moved <u>inward</u> toward the center of the state.

orchard [OHR churhd] *n.* land used for growing fruit or nut trees
　　We went to the <u>orchard</u> to pick apples.

region [REE juhn] *n.* area
　　The northern <u>region</u> of the country has many mountains.

uncertain [uhn SER tuhn] *adj.* not known; doubtful
　　Jack was <u>uncertain</u> of the answer to the teacher's question.

Word List B

adhered [ad HEERD] *v.* followed; devoted to as a supporter or follower
　　Many ancient peoples <u>adhered</u> to the belief that the world was flat.

bliss [BLIS] *n.* extreme happiness; joy
　　The couple felt <u>bliss</u> when their baby was born.

impulse [IM puhls] *n.* an incentive; a sudden urge
　　John bought several pairs of sneakers on an <u>impulse</u>.

judgments [JUJ ments] *n.* opinions formed by reason and evaluation
　　The <u>judgments</u> in the various trials were reached by different juries.

majestic [muh JES tik] *adj.* showing great dignity
　　The Statue of Liberty is a <u>majestic</u> symbol of freedom.

opinions [uh PIN yuhnz] *n.* beliefs or ideas that are not supported by direct proof
　　Each of the witnesses had different <u>opinions</u> about the accident.

seclusion [se KLOO zhuhn] *n.* isolation; the act of being removed from others
　　The patient was kept in <u>seclusion</u> until he was no longer contagious.

summoned [SUM uhnd] *v.* called together; convened
　　We were <u>summoned</u> to a meeting by our supervisor.

Name _____ Date _____

Selected Poetry of William Wordsworth
Vocabulary Warm-up Exercises

Exercise A *Fill in the blank, using each word from Word List A only once.*

We came to this [1] _____ of the country because of its famous scenic
beauty. At first, we were [2] _____ about where to go to see the beautiful
views we had read about. We found some local people to [3] _____ us,
and they helped us by taking us to the top of a large hill. We looked down from there,
and we saw farmland that included an apple [4] _____ and wheat fields.
Although some trees partially blocked our view, we occasionally had
[5] _____ of a lake in the distance. We saw this lake whenever the
[6] _____ breezes blew through the trees and moved the branches.
Turning [7] _____ and looking toward the hill directly above us, we saw a
small village nestled there. Excitedly, we climbed toward it, knowing that all to soon this
adventure would end, and we would have to return to work and the
[8] _____ that awaited us there.

Exercise B *Decide whether each of the following statements is true or false. Circle T or F, and*
explain your answer.

1. If you live in <u>seclusion</u>, you live with many family members.
   _____

2. If you <u>adhered</u> to a certain set of beliefs, you followed them.
   _____

3. It is a good idea to purchase a car on an <u>impulse</u>.
   _____

4. If you feel <u>bliss</u>, you feel great happiness.
   _____

5. <u>Judgments</u> in a court of law are made by secretaries.
   _____

6. <u>Opinions</u> are based on facts.
   _____

7. If you have been <u>summoned</u> to a meeting, you have been called to it.
   _____

8. One <u>majestic</u> symbol of royalty is the crown.
   _____

Selected Poetry of William Wordsworth
Reading Warm-up A

Read the following passage. Pay special attention to the underlined words. Then, read it again, and complete the activities. Use a separate sheet of paper for your written answers.

As my husband, John, and I walked through the apple orchard, we looked around us and took stock of our environment. We were far away from the fast pace of city life, vacationing in a region of the country known for its small-town lifestyle and striking countryside. We rented a place that was located next to a small farm, and we enjoyed walking through the fields while the gentle breezes kept us cool in the summer sun.

This was a very different lifestyle from what John and I were accustomed to. As the vice president of a small company, John's work duties included supervising a large staff and reporting important issues directly to the company's president. As a newspaper reporter, I was always out in the field, covering the stories that occurred within the bustling city. Neither of us had much free time to enjoy the outdoors.

The pace of our lives left us both exhausted, and John and I both decided that we needed a break. We were uncertain about the type of vacation we wanted. Because we were not sure about this, a friend advised us to visit this small town in the north of the country. As soon as we arrived there, we were glad that we had asked her to assist us in selecting a vacation destination. She helped us to plan the best vacation we ever had.

Aside from walking around the farm, we have also taken long hikes in the hills above it. On clear days, we caught glimpses of faraway cities where we imagined people just like us were toiling away. Turning inward and away from this view, we saw a small lake populated by many varieties of birds. This was a quiet, secluded place where we were finally able to relax. We wished our vacation could go on forever.

1. Circle the word that tells in what type of orchard John and the narrator walked. Tell what **orchard** means.

2. Circle the word that tells what region means. Use **region** in a sentence.

3. Underline the phrase that tells what the gentle breezes did. Tell what **gentle** means.

4. Underline the phrase that describes John's duties at work. Tell what **duties** means.

5. Underline the phrase that tells what uncertain means. Use **uncertain** in a sentence.

6. Circle the word that tells what assist means. Use **assist** in a sentence.

7. Underline the phrase that tells what John and the narrator caught glimpses of. Tell what **glimpses** means.

8. Underline the phrase that tells what John and the narrator saw when they turned inward and away from the view. Tell what **inward** means.

Selected Poetry of William Wordsworth
Reading Warm-up B

Read the following passage. Pay special attention to the underlined words. Then, read it again, and complete the activities. Use a separate sheet of paper for your written answers.

William Wordsworth was born in 1770, in the heart of England's <u>majestic</u> Lake District. People who love Wordsworth's poetry travel to this area to see the place that one of the founders of the Romantic Movement immortalized in his work.

Wordsworth's childhood was not full of <u>bliss</u>. His mother died when he was about eight years old, and Wordsworth's father sent him and his brothers away to boarding school. However, Wordsworth learned to thrive there. He read and wrote poetry, and he explored the beauty of the Lake District.

As an adult, Wordsworth became close friends with another Romantic poet, Samuel Taylor Coleridge. The two poets worked together to publish a collection of poems called "Lyrical Ballads." In the <u>judgments</u> of many people, this book began the English Romantic Movement. In this and later volumes, the poets <u>adhered</u> to a new style in which they used everyday language and fresh ways of looking at nature.

Wordsworth's and Coleridge's relationship was a difficult one. The poets' friendship later became strained, in part because their <u>opinions</u> about philosophy developed differently. While they continued to communicate, they were never as close as they were during the creation of "Lyrical Ballads."

Wordsworth eventually returned to live in the Lake District, where he <u>summoned</u> his creative abilities to write some of his most famous poetry about the landscape that surrounded him. Wordsworth did not write on <u>impulse</u>; he chose his words and structure carefully in order to reflect the beauty that he saw around him.

Even though Wordsworth did not live in a large city, he did not exist in <u>seclusion</u>. He was surrounded by a large family, and he was visited by influential friends. In 1843, Wordsworth was named poet laureate of England. After his death in 1850, Wordsworth was described by many as the greatest English poet that ever lived.

1. Circle the word that tells what <u>majestic</u> means. Use *majestic* in a sentence.

2. Why wasn't Wordsworth's childhood full of <u>bliss</u>? Tell what *bliss* means.

3. Underline the phrase that tells the importance of "Lyrical Ballads" in the <u>judgments</u> of many people. Tell what *judgments* means.

4. Underline the phrase that explains the news writing style to which the poets <u>adhered</u>. Tell what *adhered* means.

5. Underline the phrase that tells what happened to Wordsworth's friendship with Coleridge because their <u>opinions</u> about philosophy were different. Tell what *opinions* means.

6. Underline the phrase that tells what Wordsworth <u>summoned</u> his creative abilities to do. Tell what *summoned* means.

7. Underline the phrase that explains why Wordsworth did not write on <u>impulse</u>. Tell what *impulse* means.

8. Underline the phrase that tells why Wordsworth did not live in <u>seclusion</u>. Tell what *seclusion* means.

Name _____   Date _____

Poetry of William Wordsworth
Literary Analysis: Romanticism

During the European Enlightenment, a period that preceded Romanticism, writers and poets believed that intellect and reason were the most important aspects of humanity. They also felt that life was a universal experience for all people, no matter their background or living situation. Romanticism argued against those beliefs. Romantic poets felt that emotions were at least as important as reason, if not more so. They felt that each individual was unique, and that each person's individual life and experiences were important. They also believed that turning away from intellect and toward emotions would lead one away from society and technology and closer to nature.

DIRECTIONS: *Read the lines from the poems, and answer the questions that follow.*

> Though changed, no doubt, from what I was when first
> I came among these hills; when like a roe
> I bounded o'er the mountains, by the sides
> Of the deep rivers, and the lonely streams. . . .
> ("Tintern Abbey")

1. How does the narrator describe his younger self? What is he implying with these descriptions?

   _____

   _____

> Little we see in Nature that is ours;
> We have given our hearts away, a sordid boon! . . .
> . . . —Great God! I'd rather be
> A Pagan suckled in a creed outworn;
> So might I, standing on this pleasant lea,
> Have glimpses that would make me less forlorn;
> Have sight of Proteus rising from the sea;
> Or hear old Triton blow his wreathed horn.
> ("The World Is Too Much with Us")

2. Do you think that Wordsworth really wished he could believe in ancient Greek gods? If you do, explain why. If you don't, explain what he meant instead.

   _____

   _____

> Milton! thou should'st be living at this hour:
> England hath need of thee. . .
> . . . Thy soul was like a Star, and dwelt apart:
> Thou hadst a voice whose sound was like the sea:
> Pure as the naked heavens, majestic, free. . . .
> ("London, 1802")

Poetry of William Wordsworth
Reading Strategy: Use Literary Context

Romantic poets and writers, like Romantic musicians and artists, were revolutionary in their time. They were revolting against an earlier literary movement called the European Enlightenment. The Enlightenment stressed intellect and reason. It said that all people were essentially the same, no matter who they were or where they lived. The Romantics stressed the importance of emotions over reason, and believed in the importance of each individual's expression, based on his or her own feelings and life experiences.

DIRECTIONS: *Use this graphic organizer to help you record Romantic elements from Wordsworth's poems. When you find a passage that exemplifies Romantic ideals, think about it. Decide why it exemplifies the Romantic period rather than the European Enlightenment. One passage has already been chosen and analyzed for you.*

Passage	Why Passage Characterizes Romantic Period, Not Enlightenment
1. "But oft . . . / . . . I have owed to them / . . . sensations sweet, / Felt in the blood, and felt along the heart; / . . . feelings too / Of unremembered pleasure . . ." ("Tintern Abbey," 25–30)	It describes the emotional response that memories of the landscape provoked in the narrator rather than describing the landscape rationally and realistically.
2.	
3.	
4.	
5.	

Poetry of William Wordsworth
Vocabulary Builder

Using Related Words: *Anatomize*

A. DIRECTIONS: *Answer the following questions about* anatomize *and words related to it.*

1. What does *anatomize* mean? _____

2. What type of tool might an anatomist use? _____

3. If someone were making an anatomic study of mole rats, would she be more interested in the rats' feeding habits or in their internal organs? _____

4. In 1958, Robert Travers wrote a book called *Anatomy of a Murder.* How do you think the book treats the crime in question? _____

Using the Word List

recompense	roused	presumption	antomize
confounded	sordid	stagnant	

B. DIRECTIONS: *Each item below consists of a related pair of words in CAPITAL LETTERS followed by four lettered pairs of words. Choose the pair that best expresses a relationship similar to that expressed in the pair in capital letters. Circle the letter of your choice.*

1. EGOTIST : PRESUMPTION ::
   A. traitor : treachery
   B. doctor : stethoscope
   C. coward : bravery
   D. lawyer : summation

2. CONFOUNDED : CLEAR-HEADED ::
   A. enraged : even-tempered
   B. amused : laughing
   C. saddened : regretful
   D. wondrous : awesome

3. RECOMPENSE : SALARY ::
   A. fairness : injustice
   B. indebtedness : mortgage
   C. heat : perspiration
   D. interest : payment

4. ROUSED : EXCITED ::
   A. sympathetic : saddened
   B. curious : uninterested
   C. offended : insulted
   D. sleeping : awakened

5. SORDID : FILTHY ::
   A. frigid : lukewarm
   B. amusing : ridiculous
   C. untimely : early
   D. angry : irate

6. SWAMP : STAGNANT ::
   A. ocean : salty
   B. river : flowing
   C. pond : tidal
   D. lake : frozen

7. ANATOMIZE : DISSECT ::
   A. infantilize : mature
   B. categorize : difference
   C. prioritize : equate
   D. analyze : study

Name _____ Date _____

Poetry of William Wordsworth
Grammar and Style: Present Participial Phrases

A participle is a verb that is used as an adjective: The *folded* blanket is warmer. A present participle uses the present tense: A *rolling* stone gathers no moss. A **present participial phrase** consists of a present participle plus one or more words that modify it. The entire phrase is used as an adjective.

Example: *Walking down the street,* I ran into my friend Ken.

A. PRACTICE: *Read each of the following lines from "Lines Composed a Few Miles Above Tintern Abbey." If the underlined words are a present participial phrase, write "yes." If not, write "no" and explain why not.*

1. "And <u>passing even into my purer mind</u> / . . . feelings too/Of unremembered pleasure . . ."

   _____

2. "we are laid asleep/In body, and become a <u>living</u> soul. . . ."

   _____

3. "Have hung upon the <u>beatings of my heart</u> . . ."

   _____

4. "more like a man/<u>Flying from something</u> that he dreads . . ."

   _____

5. "The <u>sounding</u> cataract/Haunted me like a passion . . ."

   _____

B. Writing Application: *Rewrite each of the following sentences, adding a present participial phrase that modifies the subject.*

1. I lost my key.

   _____

2. That dog looks like my dog.

   _____

3. The car is out of control.

   _____

4. The man seems familiar.

   _____

5. The movie is great!

   _____

Poetry of William Wordsworth
Support for Writing

Use the organizer below to take notes for a response to criticism. Review the poems, and then write notes and cite lines that support or argue against Thomas Wolfe's statement.

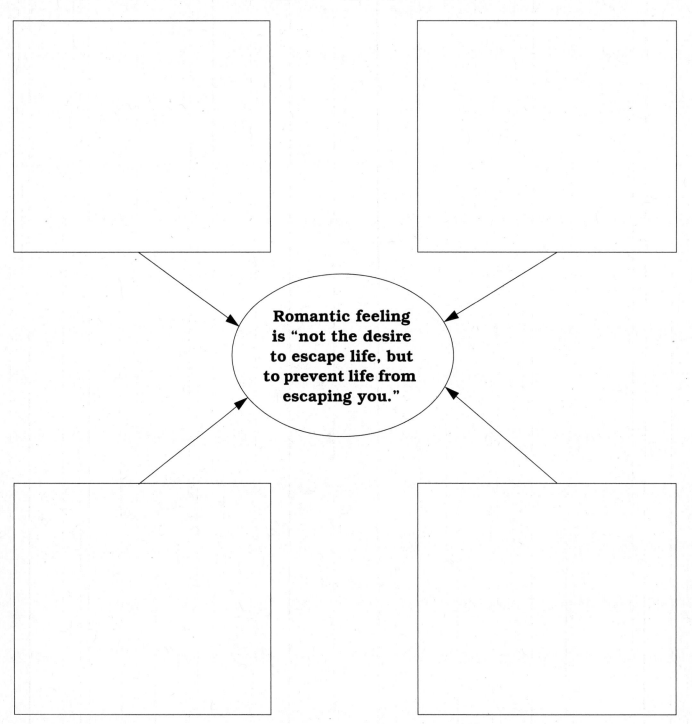

Romantic feeling is "not the desire to escape life, but to prevent life from escaping you."

On a separate page, write a response to criticism. Clearly state whether or not you agree with Wolfe. Then, use evidence from the organizer to support your position.

Poetry of William Wordsworth
Support for Extend Your Learning

Listening and Speaking

Use the chart to collect technical and informal words and phrases to describe your pieces of Romantic art in a **photo essay presentation.**

Artwork	Technical and Informal Descriptive Words and Phrases

Research and Technology

Write the name of the environmental group you have chosen in the center circle. Write Romantic influences on the group in the surrounding circles. Use the information to complete your **cultural analysis.**

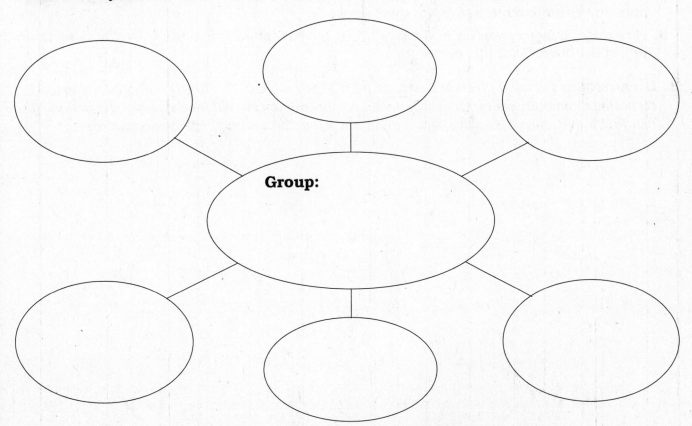

Group:

Poetry of William Wordsworth
Enrichment: Social Studies

Before about 1770, most people in England lived on small farms, where family members tended the livestock or raised the crops. Some people were craftworkers, such as shoemakers, blacksmiths, and glassblowers. They worked in their own shops and made things that they sold directly to other people. Girls learned to cook, spin, and sew from their mothers. If a boy wanted to learn a craft, he often learned from his father. If he wanted to do something other than what his father did, he became an apprentice. An apprentice lived with a craftworker for a number of years to learn the craft from his master. When he was good enough, he went out and set up his own shop. Apprentices were given room and board, but no salary. It was very rare for someone to pay another person to work for him.

In the late 1700s, the Industrial Revolution changed all of this. Technological advancements made factories possible for the first time. These factories spun wool and made cloth. Huge machines could turn out much more material than could a person working on a small hand-powered machine. Still, people were needed to run the machines, and factory owners paid people for such work. As more and more factories were built, more and more people left the countryside to live in cities where there were factory jobs. Before this time, people had spent most or all of the day outside. Now many people spent their entire day inside, surrounded by large, dirty, smoky machines.

A. DIRECTIONS: *Answer the following questions on a separate sheet of paper.*

1. Imagine that you are a young factory worker in the late 1700s. How is the place where you work different from the place your parents and grandparents worked?

2. How might the feelings you have about your work be different from the feelings your parents and grandparents had about their work?

3. How might a factory worker in the late 1700s have responded to a poem by Wordsworth or one of the other Romantic poets?

B. DIRECTIONS: *Create a timeline that runs from 1750 to 1850. The timeline should show works by various Romantic poets, as well as technological advances and inventions of the period. You can find information about the period in an encyclopedia and other reference sources.*

Poetry of William Wordsworth
Selection Test A

Critical Reading *Identify the letter of the choice that best answers the question.*

____ 1. Which line from "Lines Composed a Few Miles Above Tintern Abbey" best describes Wordsworth's response to nature when he had visited the abbey five years earlier?
   A. Nature was a passion and intense love.
   B. Nature was less appealing than city life.
   C. Nature was not interesting to him.
   D. Nature was a cold and threatening place.

____ 2. With whom did Wordsworth visit Tintern Abbey?
   A. his wife
   B. Samuel Taylor Coleridge
   C. his sister Dorothy
   D. Robert Southey

____ 3. What is the main theme of "Lines Composed a Few Miles Above Tintern Abbey"?
   A. the glories and triumphs of youth
   B. the power of nature to renew the spirit
   C. the rewards of the imagination
   D. the strength of humans

____ 4. Which characteristic of "Lines Composed a Few Miles Above Tintern Abbey" shows that it is a Romantic poem?
   A. the outdoor, natural setting
   B. the speaker's emphasis on the importance of the individual
   C. the use of the narrative format
   D. the description of the speaker's emotional response to nature

____ 5. Which lines best state the theme of the excerpt from *The Prelude*?
   A. "But to be young was very Heaven!"
   B. "But in the very world . . . the place where, in the end, / We find our happiness . . ."
   C. "I lost / All feeling of conviction. . . ."
   D. "They who had fed their childhood upon dreams, / The play-fellows of fancy. . . ."

____ 6. According to the speaker in *The Prelude*, why did the French Revolution fail?
   A. Other nations entered the war and defeated the revolutionaries.
   B. The war of self-defense became a war of oppression.
   C. The revolution was poorly organized and soon broke down.
   D. The revolutionaries did not know how to run the government.

____ 7. What is the meaning of the title of the poem "The World Is Too Much with Us"?
   A. The world is a vast place that we must each face alone.
   B. Living is a great trial that can be overwhelming.
   C. Our lives are too short, and we do not accomplish much.
   D. We spend too much time working for material things.

____ 8. Which of these characteristics of "The World Is Too Much with Us" shows that it is a lyric poem?
   A. It mentions several mythological characters.
   B. It has many references to God and religion.
   C. It implies that understanding nature leads to self-awareness.
   D. It does not follow a regular pattern of end rhymes.

____ 9. What does the speaker in "London, 1802" mean by saying that England is in need of Milton?
   A. England needs manners, freedom, and power.
   B. English poetry has become dull and uninspired.
   C. The French Revolution has failed to bring freedom.
   D. England needs someone to write an epic.

Vocabulary and Grammar

____ 10. Which vocabulary word best completes the following sentence?

   The excitement of the revolution _____ people, and they demanded freedoms they had never before dared to think about.

   A. roused
   B. confounded
   C. anatomized
   D. recompensed

____ **11.** Which word means the same as *sordid* in this line from "The World Is Too Much with Us"?

> Little we see in Nature that is ours;
> We have given our hearts away, a *sordid* boon!

   A. double

   B. fortunate

   C. dirty

   D. reasonable

____ **12.** Which line from "Lines Composed a Few Miles Above Tintern Abbey" contains a present participial phrase?

   A. "Almost suspended, we are laid asleep in body, and become a living soul."

   B. "These waters, rolling from their mountain springs / With a soft inland murmur."

   C. "not only with the sense of present pleasure, but with pleasing thoughts. . . ."

   D. "When like a roe / I bounded o'er the mountains."

Essay

13. Write an essay in which you summarize Wordsworth's feelings toward nature as expressed in "Lines Composed a Few Miles Above Tintern Abbey." First, explain the feelings he had five years earlier. How did his feelings change in the years since then? Is nature still important to him? In what way? Use examples from "Lines Composed a Few Miles Above Tintern Abbey" to support your response.

14. Choose one or more of the poems. In an essay, explain how Wordsworth's poems demonstrate some of the qualities of Romanticism. Discuss at least two of these qualities of Romanticism: simplicity and directness of language; expression of spontaneous, intensified feelings; profound responses to nature; and diction. Give examples from the poems to support your discussion.

Name _____ Date _____

Poetry of William Wordsworth
Selection Test B

Critical Reading *Identify the letter of the choice that best completes the statement or answers the question.*

_____ 1. Which phrase best summarizes the predominant theme of "Lines Composed a Few Miles Above Tintern Abbey"?
   A. the wondrous and fleeting emotions of childhood
   B. the renewing and uplifting power of nature
   C. the educational and religious benefits of solitude
   D. the kind and simple ways of the common folk

_____ 2. Wordsworth's image "of some hermit's cave, where by his fire / The hermit sits alone" could be said to reflect the Romantics' rejection of the Neoclassical emphasis on _____.
   A. society
   B. religion
   C. extremity
   D. emotion

_____ 3. In "Lines Composed a Few Miles Above Tintern Abbey," Wordsworth describes his second visit to the abbey as more _____ than the first.
   A. emotional
   B. memorable
   C. depressing
   D. reflective

_____ 4. "Lines Composed a Few Miles Above Tintern Abbey" is a poem that celebrates the power of _____.
   A. analysis
   B. deduction
   C. memory
   D. prophecy

_____ 5. Which lines most directly express Wordsworth's interest in the discovery of the mystical or the supernatural through nature?
   A. "His little, nameless, unremembered, acts / Of kindness and of love."
   B. "I cannot paint / what then I was. The sounding cataract / Haunted me like a passion . . ."
   C. ". . . not as in the hour / Of thoughtless youth; but hearing oftentimes / The still, sad music of humanity . . ."
   D. ". . . a sense sublime / Of something . . . / Whose dwelling is the light of setting suns . . ."

_____ 6. "Lines Composed a Few Miles Above Tintern Abbey" is easy to recognize as a Romantic poem because it
   A. describes the narrator's emotions about a landscape.
   B. is about a revolution.
   C. takes place entirely outdoors.
   D. argues for the importance of the individual.

_____ 7. At the end of "The World Is Too Much With Us," Wordsworth demonstrates by his example the Romantic belief in the
   A. helpful influence of formal worship.
   B. critical need for universal equality.
   C. transforming power of the mind.
   D. enduring worth of ancient literature.

_____ 8. What is Wordsworth's main subject in "The World Is Too Much With Us"?
   A. the frenzied quest for wealth
   B. the decline of classical learning
   C. the rise of industrial cities
   D. the wanton destruction of nature

_____ 9. Which sentence best describes how the Romantic ideal applies to these lines from "London, 1802"?
   Oh! raise us up, return to us again;
   And give us manners, virtue, freedom, power.
   A. Romantics believed humanity needed a great leader.
   B. Romantics believed in the power of the arts to improve humanity.
   C. Romantics believed the arts were better in the past, before they turned away from nature.
   D. Romantics believed humanity was better in the past, before it turned away from nature.

_____ 10. Which lines best summarize the theme of the excerpt from *The Prelude*?
   A. "I lost / All feeling of conviction"
   B. "I . . . toiled, intent / To anatomize the frame of social life. . . ."
   C. "I adhered / More firmly to the old tenets. . . ."
   D. "O pleasant exercise of hope and joy!"

_____ 11. Why might a Romantic poet like Wordsworth have supported the French Revolution at first?
   A. The Revolutionaries claimed to support the rights and importance of individuals.
   B. The Revolutionaries advocated a return to nature.
   C. The Revolutionaries were opposed to technology.
   D. The leaders of the Revolution were poets and writers.

_____ 12. Which sentence best describes Romanticism's attitude toward emotions?
   A. They are an important part of life and an important tool for an artist.
   B. They are an important part of life but should not be emphasized in art.
   C. They will lead people toward technology and away from nature.
   D. They help people appreciate nature.

Vocabulary and Grammar

____ 13. Which word means the opposite of *sordid*?
   A. random
   B. exactly
   C. unarmed
   D. clean

____ 14. What does the word *confounded* mean?
   A. bound together
   B. confused or bewildered
   C. infernal
   D. established at the same time

____ 15. What is a participle?
   A. an adjective that is used as a verb
   B. a verb form that is used as an adjective
   C. a noun that is used as a verb
   D. a verb form that is used as a noun

____ 16. Which italicized phrase is an example of a present participial phrase?
   A. "As if they had within some *lurking* right / To wield it . . ."
   B. "betrayed / By present objects, and by *reasonings false* . . ."
   C. "more like a man / *Flying from something that he dreads* . . ."
   D. "little lines / Of sportive wood *run wild* . . ."

Essay

17. In "The World Is Too Much With Us," Wordsworth expressed concern for the society in which he lived. He felt it had gone astray and explained how in the poem. Write an essay discussing his concerns. What were they? How did he express them? If he were alive today, might he have the same concerns for our society?

18. In "Lines Composed a Few Miles Above Tintern Abbey," the narrator revisits the area where he grew up. In the excerpt from *The Prelude*, Wordsworth describes his attitude toward the French Revolution. Each poem describes a change that occurred over time. Write an essay comparing and contrasting the two works. In each case, what was it that changed? What attitude was expressed about the changes? How are the two works similar? How are they different?

Unit 4: Rebels and Dreamers
Benchmark Test 7

MULTIPLE CHOICE

Literary Analysis and Reading Skills

1. Which of these aspects of English Romanticism is reflected by a writer's use of dialect?
   A. a love of nature
   B. the loss of faith in reason
   C. a celebration of the common people
   D. an emphasis on intense feelings

2. What is the main purpose an author would have for using symbols?
   A. to provide a concrete example of something intangible
   B. to support a point by providing specific details
   C. to appeal to the reader's emotions
   D. to create an unresolved puzzle

3. Which aspect of English Romanticism is reflected most in the Gothic tradition?
   A. a love of nature
   B. a loss of faith in reason
   C. a celebration of common folk
   D. an emphasis on simple language

4. Which characteristic is typical of a lyric poem?
   A. It has more than one speaker.
   B. It expresses loss of faith in both science and reason.
   C. It tells a story.
   D. It conveys personal emotions and observations.

Read "John Anderson, My Jo" by Robert Burns, below. Then, answer the questions that follow.

John Anderson, my jo°, John,	° **jo** sweetheart
When we were first acquent;	
Your locks were like the raven,	
Your bonnie° brow was brent°;	° **bonnie** attractive ° **brent** smooth
5 But now your brow is bald, John,	
Your locks are like the snow;	
But blessings on your frosty pow,°	° **pow** head
John Anderson, my jo.	
John Anderson, my jo, John,	
10 We clamb the hill thegither;	
And mony a cantie° day, John,	° **cantie** happy
We've had w' ane anither:	
Now we maun totter down, John,	
And hand in hand we'll go,	
15 And sleep thegither at the foot,	
John Anderson, my jo.	

5. What chief emotions does the speaker of this lyric poem express?
   A. love for John Anderson and a wistful acceptance of their aging
   B. sorrow for John Anderson's death and regret that Anderson never knew the speaker's love
   C. admiration for the young John Anderson and disappointment with the old one
   D. jealousy and anger toward John Anderson, who stole the speaker's sweetheart years ago

6. What does the use of dialect emphasize about the speaker and John Anderson?
   A. They are immigrants learning how to live in a new land.
   B. They are an old-fashioned couple who are very set in their ways.
   C. They are simple people who have led a simple life together.
   D. They live close to the land and take comfort from nature.

7. In the Scottish dialect of the poem, what do lines 11–12 mean?
   A. And money on happy days, John, or at least we have had each other.
   B. And many a happy day, John, we've had with one another.
   C. And others wished for the happy days, John, that we had with one another.
   D. Although we've had happy days, John, we've asked for yet another.

8. From the details in the second stanza, what does the hill seem to be a symbol of?
   A. nature
   B. hardship
   C. fame
   D. life

Read "A Poison Tree" by William Blake, below. Then, answer the questions that follow.

> I was angry with my friend:
> I told my wrath, my wrath did end.
> I was angry with my foe:
> I told it not, my wrath did grow.
>
> 5 And I watered it in fears,
> Night and morning with my tears;
> And I sunnèd it with smiles,
> And with soft deceitful wiles.
>
> And it grew both day and night,
> 10 Till it bore an apple bright.
> And my foe beheld it shine,
> And he knew that it was mine,
>
> And into my garden stole,
> When the night had veiled the pole;°   ° **pole:** sky; heavens
> 15 In the morning glad I see
> My foe outstretched beneath the tree.

9. What main observation does the speaker make in this poem?
   A. Expressing anger does less damage than holding it in.
   B. It is easier to express feelings to your friends than to people you do not know.
   C. If you are patient, you can get revenge on your enemies.
   D. It is usually a good idea to hide your feelings.

10. Which of these elements in the poem most clearly symbolizes the speaker's hatred?
    A. the night
    B. the tears
    C. the smiles
    D. the apple tree

11. To accompany the poem, Blake drew a picture of a man outstretched beneath a tree. What would this visual element stress about the poem?
    A. the dramatic death of the enemy at the poem's end
    B. the speaker's final forgiveness of his enemy
    C. the enemy's satisfaction and contentment after eating the apple
    D. the comfort that the speaker takes in natural events and scenes

Read this selection from Wuthering Heights, *a novel by nineteenth-century British author Emily Brontë. Then, answer the questions that follow.*

Yesterday afternoon set in misty and cold. I had half a mind to spend it by my study fire, instead of wading through heath[1] and mud to Wuthering Heights. [Nevertheless,] I took my hat, and, after a four miles' walk, arrived at Heathcliff's garden gate just in time to escape the first feathery flakes of a snow shower.

On that bleak hilltop the earth was hard with a black frost, and the air made me shiver through every limb. Being unable to remove the chain, I jumped over, and, running up the flagged causeway bordered with straggling gooseberry bushes, knocked vainly for admittance, till my knuckles tingled, and the dogs howled. . . .

12. What aspects of the setting show the influence of the Gothic tradition?
    A. It is simple and rural.
    B. It includes a sheep farm.
    C. It is humble and shabby.
    D. It is forbidding and frightening.

13. Based on the selection details, what do you predict Heathcliff will be like?
    A. happy-go-lucky
    B. creepy and troubled
    C. childlike and innocent
    D. rich and bored

Read these stanzas from "The Tables Turned" by William Wordsworth. Then, answer the questions that follow.

One impulse from a vernal° wood   ° **vernal** related to spring
May teach you more of man,
Of moral evil and of good,
Than all the sages can.

5 Sweet is the lore which Nature brings;
Our meddling intellect
Misshapes the beauteous forms of thing:
We murder to dissect.

Enough of Science and of Art;
10 Close up these barren leaves;
Come forth, and bring with you a heart
That watches and receives.

14. What Romantic message about nature do the stanzas convey?
    A. Nature does not care about human suffering.
    B. Nature can be menacing as well as comforting.
    C. Nature is the best teacher.
    D. Nature renews itself every year.

15. Which of these qualities of English Romanticism do the stanzas display?
    A. celebration of common people
    B. an admiration for nature
    C. loss of faith in reason and science
    D. interest in the supernatural

16. How does the speaker's style reflect the influence of English Romanticism?
    A. He uses direct language to express strong feelings.
    B. He is thoughtful and unemotional.
    C. He speaks spontaneously, without much thought.
    D. He is scientific and scholarly.

17. Which of the following is a quality of an effective guidebook?
    A. It includes fictional information as well as facts about its subject.
    B. It focuses on expressing strong personal feelings about its subject.
    C. It provides historical and practical information about its subject.
    D. It does not include any sort of illustration or graphic aid.

18. What do you call a drawing or plan that breaks down a larger topic by indicating all parts and explaining the relationship between them?
    A. a dialect
    B. an essay
    C. a diagram
    D. a guidebook

Vocabulary

19. Based on your understanding of the root *-spir-*, which phrase would best replace the word *inspire*?
    - A. to breathe into
    - B. to draw a circle
    - C. to take place
    - D. to add air to

20. To *loathe* is to find hateful or disgusting. Which of these do you think most people find *loathsome*?
    - A. an ugly insect
    - B. a skillful painting
    - C. a humorous comic
    - D. a gorgeous view

21. Based on your knowledge of the suffix *-some*, which meaning would you choose for the word *worrisome*?
    - A. annoying
    - B. final
    - C. tending to create anxiety
    - D. in a repeating pattern

22. Which of these words is related to the word *phantasm*?
    - A. fantastic
    - B. pharmacy
    - C. fan
    - D. frantic

23. From your understanding of words that come from the Greek *atomos*, what do you think an *atomizer* is?
    - A. a ghostly presence
    - B. a person who expresses doubt or uncertainty about something
    - C. a breathless wind
    - D. a device that shoots out a spray of small particles

Grammar

24. Identify the interjection or interjections that should be set off by commas in this sentence.

    Perhaps I will perform well and gee maybe win a prize.

    - A. *perhaps* only
    - B. *perhaps* and *gee*
    - C. *well* and *gee*
    - D. *gee* only

25. In which sentence is the italicized verb used correctly?
    A. When the curtain *rised*, the show began.
    B. The play *raised* some interesting questions.
    C. The stars of the play had *rose* to the occasion.
    D. Everyone *raised* up when the play ended.

26. Which sentence contains a past participial phrase?
    A. Robert Burns is known as the Voice of Scotland.
    B. Many of his poems were written in Scottish dialect.
    C. Born in poverty, Burns never received a formal education.
    D. He published his first collection of poems in 1786.

27. Which sentence contains a present participial phrase?
    A. Published anonymously, Joanna Baillie's book of plays created a strong reaction in London.
    B. No one guessed that the book was written by a quiet thirty-eight-year-old woman.
    C. Baillie had enjoyed putting on plays since she was a girl.
    D. Moving to London, she and her sisters enjoyed the literary scene there.

28. Which noun in this sentence does the participial phrase modify?

    Wordsworth, working with Coleridge, published his groundbreaking poetry at the end of the eighteenth century.

    A. Wordsworth
    B. Coleridge
    C. poetry
    D. century

ESSAY

29. Think of two poems that portray two people with something in common. Either person may be the speaker of the poem, a person that the poem describes, or a character in a narrative poem. Then, on your paper or a separate sheet, write a brief essay comparing and contrasting the two characters.

30. Think of a work you have read or seen that would qualify as part of the Gothic tradition. Then, on your paper or a separate sheet, write a brief essay giving your impressions before and after you read or saw the work.

31. The French poet Charles Baudelaire once said, "Romanticism is found precisely neither in the choice of subjects nor in exact truth, but in a way of feeling." What do you think he means? Do you think his observation is true? React to Baudelaire's statement in a short essay that you write on your paper or a separate sheet.

Unit 4: Rebels and Dreamers
Diagnostic Test 8

MULTIPLE CHOICE

Read the selection. Then, answer the questions that follow.

Ancient epics do more than tell stories about fantastic adventures. Many ancient epics are in the form of a narrative poem. Because many epics were originally passed down orally, they contain repetitions of stock phrases to help the storyteller remember the story. In most ancient epics, the hero embodies the sort of moral attributes that are admired in their culture, such as bravery, selflessness, and strength.

In ancient epics such as the *Ramayana* and the *Iliad,* we meet heroes who go through relentless trials that test their endurance and strength as they pursue something extremely valuable. In the *Ramayana,* a Sanskrit epic written by Valmike, the hero suffers banishment while he pursues perfect virtue. In the *Iliad,* a Greek epic by Homer, the hero pursues victory in war.

Usually there are supernatural forces arrayed both for and against the hero. In the *Ramayana,* the hero must thwart a demon that threatens both him and a wise sage. In the *Iliad,* the Greek gods and goddesses intervene to help their favorite warriors.

In most epics, the hero ultimately achieves his goals. His success is vital to the development of his culture. For example, in the *Aeneid* by Virgil, Aeneas founds the society that will become the Roman Empire. Sometimes, the hero becomes the savior of his people, rescuing them from destruction.

1. Which of the following general statements best applies to ancient epics?
   A. They contain many fantastic adventures.
   B. They were written long ago.
   C. The hero pursues something valuable.
   D. The hero always achieves his goals.

2. Which of the following is always contained in ancient epics?
   A. heroes who undergo trials
   B. fantastic adventures
   C. some humor
   D. happy endings

3. Who composed the *Ramayana*?
   A. Homer
   B. Aeneas
   C. Virgil
   D. Valmike

4. Which of the following best explains how the hero of an epic reflects his culture?
   A. He usually spreads his cultural ideas to others.
   B. He embodies attributes important in his culture.
   C. He dresses and behaves in the manner of his people.
   D. He is usually an important ruler in his culture.

5. Which of the following best describes the role that the supernatural plays in ancient epics?
   A. Supernatural beings usually help or try to harm the hero.
   B. The hero usually possesses some type of supernatural power.
   C. The hero is usually a spiritual person who frequently prays.
   D. The hero often has one parent who is a supernatural being.

6. From which culture did the epic the *Aeneid* originate?
   A. Sanskrit
   B. Indian
   C. Greek
   D. Roman

7. What does the hero of the *Aeneid* achieve?
   A. perfect virtue
   B. the establishment of a new society
   C. victory in war
   D. the blessings of the gods

8. What might you expect to find in ancient epics that were originally passed down orally?
   A. a great deal of dialogue
   B. words that have musical qualities
   C. repetition of the same phrases throughout
   D. many lines of poetry that rhyme

Read the selection. Then, answer the questions that follow.

One of the greatest epics in all of world literature, the *Ramayana* tells the story of the Sanskrit hero, Rama. After Rama wins his wife, Sita, by performing a feat of great strength, his father decides to make him king. However, Rama's stepmother reminds Rama's father that years before he made a promise to do her bidding after she saved his life. Now, she asks him to keep that promise by making her own son king and banishing Rama for fourteen years. Rama departs, accompanied by Sita and his brother Lakshman.

The three travelers enter the jungles of India, where the presiding rulers are evil magicians known as Rakshas. When a young Raksha woman falls in love with Rama, Lakshman cuts off the Raksha woman's nose. To their misfortune, she is the sister of Rava, the king of the Rakshas, who wreaks his revenge by capturing Sita and taking her far away.

Rama and Lakshman enlist the aid of the Monkey God, who sends monkeys far and wide to search for Sita. When she is eventually found in Ceylon, Rama, Lakshman, and the monkeys defeat the Rakshas. Sita and Rama are reunited, and the two become the model for happy, virtuous couples throughout the land.

9. What is the subject of the *Ramayana*?
   A. the trials of the hero Rama
   B. the beauty and virtue of Sita
   C. the loyalty of Lakshman
   D. the evil and malice of the Raksha

10. Why did Rama's stepmother wish to have him banished?
    A. She feared he had become too strong.
    B. She did not wish him to marry Sita.
    C. She wanted her own son to be king.
    D. She was jealous of him.

11. Who accompanied Rama on his travels?
    A. Sita and Rakshas
    B. Sita and Lakshman
    C. Lakshman and the Monkey God
    D. Lakshman and Rakshas

12. Who were the Rakshas?
    A. evil magicians
    B. companions of Rama
    C. rulers of Ceylon
    D. worshipers of the Monkey God

13. Which of the following best explains how Rama and his companions offended the Rakshas?

   A. They entered the jungles of India without permission of the Rakshas.

   B. Lakshman refused the love of a Raksha woman.

   C. Rama refused the love of a Raksha woman.

   D. Lakshman cut off the nose of a Raksha woman.

14. What revenge did the Raksha king take on Rama?

   A. He kidnapped Lakshman.

   B. He kidnapped Sita.

   C. He cut off Sita's nose.

   D. He sent the Monkey King to destroy him.

15. How did Rama defeat the Rakshas?

   A. with the help of soldiers of Ceylon

   B. by using Raksha magic against them

   C. with the help of the monkeys

   D. by destroying the Monkey God

Study these words from the selections. Then, complete the activities that follow.

Word List A

ancient [AYN chuhnt] *adj.* very old
  The ancient statue was more than one thousand years old.

blossomed [BLAH suhmd] *v.* bloomed; flourished
  The bud blossomed into a beautiful flower.

burst [BERST] *v.* came apart suddenly
  The balloon burst when Jack pricked it with a pin.

glorious [GLOHR ee uhs] *adj.* marked by great beauty; magnificent
  The glorious day was sunny and warm.

harbor [HAHR buhr] *n.* a sheltered part of a body of water deep enough to anchor ships
  The boat pulled into the harbor, and the sailors unloaded its cargo.

merry [MEHR ee] *adj.* delightful; jolly
  The merry man sang many happy songs.

pleasure [PLE zhuhr] *n.* delight
  Listening to classical music gives me great pleasure.

sheen [SHEEN] *n.* sparkling brightness; shininess
  The sheen on the water was caused by the reflection of the sun.

Word List B

agony [AG uh nee] *n.* suffering; intense physical or emotional pain
  The injured soldier lay in agony until help arrived.

chasm [KAZ uhm] *n.* a deep crack or divide
  The chasm in the road was caused by the earthquake.

din [DIN] *n.* a mixture of loud, confusing, and disagreeable noises
  The din of the party made it difficult to follow the conversation.

howled [HOWLD] *v.* cried loudly
  The dog howled at the door until someone let it inside.

mariner [MAR i nuhr] *n.* a sailor
  The mariner sailed the ship across the Atlantic Ocean.

mingled [MING uhld] *v.* combined; mixed
  The guests mingled with the hospital staff at the reception.

plagued [PLAYGD] *v.* annoyed; distressed
  Sally was plagued by a terrible cold during her vacation.

prayer [PRAYR] *n.* an act of communion with God or another deity in the form of confession, praise, or thanksgiving.
  The congregation offered a prayer in support of the suffering family.

"The Rime of the Ancient Mariner" and **"Kubla Khan"** by Samuel Taylor Coleridge
Vocabulary Warm-up Exercises

Exercise A *Fill in the blank, using each word from Word List A only once.*

The [1] _____ city has existed for thousands of years. It is located next to
the great [2] _____, where many ships from around the world stop to
receive new supplies. This city is [3] _____ and beautiful because of its
location and its architecture. The [4] _____ on the water makes the whole
area bright. It is a [5] _____ to walk the cool, tree-lined streets and to
look at the beautiful buildings and gardens. It is especially nice to visit in the spring,
when all of the colorful flowers have [6] _____ and filled the gardens
with color. The people who live here are a [7] _____ group, and they are
happy because they know that they live in a beautiful place. Thus, they were greatly
saddened by the destruction that was caused when a tower filled with water
[8] _____ and flooded most of the city.

Exercise B *Decide whether each statement is true or false. Circle* T *or* F, *and explain your
answer.*

1. If you are <u>plagued</u> by someone, you are annoyed by them.
   _____

2. <u>Prayer</u> is an idea, thought, or statement offered to God or another deity.
   _____

3. A <u>mariner</u> drives a truck.
   _____

4. Breaking a bone would put you in <u>agony</u>.
   _____

5. You would hear a <u>din</u> in the library.
   _____

6. A <u>chasm</u> is a steep mountain.
   _____

7. If you <u>mingled</u> with people at a party, you mixed with them.
   _____

8. If a baby has <u>howled</u> for his supper, he has cried for it.
   _____

"The Rime of the Ancient Mariner" and **"Kubla Khan"** by Samuel Taylor Coleridge
Reading Warm-up A

Read the following passage. Pay special attention to the underlined words. Then, read it again, and complete the activities. Use a separate sheet of paper for your written answers.

The passengers alighted from the airplane and into a glorious day on the tropical island. Beauty was every-where. To their right, they saw a harbor filled with crystal blue water and cruise ships that were anchored there. To their left, they viewed endless gardens in which colorful flowers blossomed and filled the air with their exotic fra-grance. Many of the airplane passengers were tourists who were visiting this place because of its famous beaches, beautiful scenery, and hospitality. Looking around, they felt like they had truly entered a paradise.

Throughout the island, visitors had the opportunity to relax on sandy, white beaches or to tour ancient cities that have existed for hundreds of years. Friendly native islanders catered to their needs and wants. No one was dissatisfied with the service or attention that was given.

What these tourists did not see behind the sheen of happy faces and lush scenery was the poverty in which many of the islanders lived. Many residents had no elec-tricity or running water in their own homes, even though all of the areas that served the tourists did. Government officials made sure that this part of island life was well hidden from tourists, because they were afraid that it would discourage people from visiting. After all, they rea-soned, people traveled to the island for purposes of pleasure, not social justice. Knowing about these prob-lems would interfere with their enjoyment of their trip. This other life on the island was located far away from the hotels and beaches, and no visitors ever found it.

Thus, if the passing visitor dared to look into the eyes of the merry tour guide who showed her the sights of the island, perhaps she would see the suffering that existed there. Then, her views about the island would have burst, once she realized the truth about how the island-ers really lived.

1. Circle the word that tells what glorious means. Use *glorious* in a sentence.

2. Underline the phrase that tells with what the harbor was filled. Tell what *harbor* means.

3. Underline the phrase that tells what occurred after the flowers had blossomed. Tell what *blossomed* means.

4. Underline the phrase that supports the idea that the cities on the island were ancient. Tell what *ancient* means.

5. Underline the phrase that tells what was behind the sheen. Tell what *sheen* means.

6. Circle the word that tells what pleasure means. Use *pleasure* in a sentence.

7. Underline the phrase that tells what a visitor would have found if she looked into the eyes of a merry islander. Tell what *merry* means.

8. Underline the phrase that tells what would have burst if the truth about the islanders' situation was known. Tell what *burst* means.

"The Rime of the Ancient Mariner" and **"Kubla Khan"** by Samuel Taylor Coleridge
Reading Warm-up B

Read the following passage. Pay special attention to the underlined words. Then, read it again, and complete the activities. Use a separate sheet of paper for your written answers.

Samuel Taylor Coleridge is regarded as one of the founders of the Romantic Movement of the eighteenth and nineteenth centuries. Many of Coleridge's written works contain images phrases, and words that are still heard within the <u>din</u> of the modern English language. Moreover, his work still influences poetry that is written today.

"Rime of the Ancient <u>Mariner</u>" is one of Coleridge's most famous poems. It is a long poem about a sailor whose act of killing an albatross <u>plagued</u> him and his shipmates. In this poem, Coleridge describes the <u>agony</u> suffered by these characters in great detail. The sailors would have <u>howled</u> in pain if they were able to, but as it was, they were too thirsty. It is from this image that Coleridge describes the lack of water to drink. Through time, Coleridge's words have <u>mingled</u> with others, and the famous misquote now reads "Water, water everywhere, and not a drop to drink." The phrase "sadder but wiser man" was also taken from this poem, and it has gained fame independent of it.

Coleridge has also contributed to the English language through introduction of new words. In this way, he attempted to bridge the <u>chasm</u> between ideas and ways to express them. For instance, he introduced the word *aesthetic,* which means "relating to the sense of the beautiful," to the English language through his literary criticism.

While Coleridge was not interested in religious <u>prayer</u>, he was very involved in learning about philosophy. As a youth, he studied German philosophy, and he returned to this passion later in life. This interest also influenced the poetry and literary criticisms that he produced.

Notably, Coleridge was able to have a great impact on English language and poetry. He continued to contribute to English language and literature until his death.

1. Underline the phrase that tells what Coleridge's work has produced that is still heard in the <u>din</u> of the modern English language. Tell what *din* means.

2. Circle the word that tells what <u>mariner</u> means. Use *mariner* in a sentence.

3. Underline the phrase that tells how the mariner and his shipmates were <u>plagued</u> by the killing of the albatross. Tell what *plagued* means.

4. Underline the phrase that tells how Coleridge described the <u>agony</u> of the characters. Tell what *agony* means.

5. Would the sailors have <u>howled</u> in pain if they were able to? Why didn't they?

6. Underline the phrase that tells what the result was after the original phrase in the poem <u>mingled</u> with other words. Tell what *mingled* means.

7. What <u>chasm</u> did Coleridge try to bridge with his introduction of new words into the English language? Tell what *chasm* means.

8. Underline the phrase that explains what Coleridge was interested in if he was not interested in <u>prayer</u>. Tell what *prayer* means.

Name _____ Date _____

"The Rime of the Ancient Mariner" and "Kubla Khan" by Samuel Taylor Coleridge
Literary Analysis: Poetic Sound Devices

Alliteration is the repetition of a consonant sound at the beginnings of words. **Consonance** is the repetition of consonant sounds in stressed syllables with dissimilar vowel sounds. **Assonance** is repetition of vowel sounds in stressed syllables with dissimilar consonant sounds. **Internal rhyme** is the use of rhyming words within a line.

DIRECTIONS: *In each of the following passages from "The Rime of the Ancient Mariner" and "Kubla Kahn," certain letters are italicized. For each passage, write on the line the* **sound device** *that is used.*

1. "As who pursued with ye*ll* and b*l*ow" _____

2. "The ice did spli*t* with a thunder-fi*t*" _____

3. "*H*e *h*olds *h*im with *h*is skinny *h*and" _____

4. "The ship was ch*eered*, the harbor cl*eared*" _____

5. "And we did spea*k* only to brea*k*" _____

6. "*R*ed as a *r*ose is she" _____

7. "All in a h*ot* and c*o*pper sky" _____

8. "The Wedding G*u*est he beat his br*east*" _____

9. "The death fires danced at n*ight*" _____

10. "The *f*air breeze blew, the white *f*oam *f*lew" _____

11. "His *f*lashing eyes, his *f*loating hair!" _____

12. "A *d*amsel with a *d*ulcimer" _____

13. "For *h*e on *h*oneydew *h*ath fed," _____

14. "And close your eyes with h*o*ly dread" _____

15. "And from this chasm, with *c*easeless turmoil *s*e*ething*" _____

"The Rime of the Ancient Mariner" and **"Kubla Khan"** by Samuel Taylor Coleridge

Reading Strategy: Analyze Poetic Effects

One of the primary characteristics that sets verse apart from prose is the range of poetic and sound devices commonly used in poetry. These devices enhance the musical qualities of the language by pleasing the ear, but they also serve to emphasize meaning and create mood. By paying attention to these devices you can become more sensitive to the nuances and effects of poetic language. The following are several different types of sound devices:

alliteration: repetition of consonant sounds at the beginnings of words

consonance: repetition of consonant sounds at the ends of words

assonance: repetition of vowel sounds in nearby words or syllables

internal rhyme: rhymes occurring within a poetic line

ordinary repetition: repetition of entire words

DIRECTIONS: *Use this chart to keep track of poetic effects as you read "The Rime of the Ancient Mariner" and "Kubla Khan." Each time you encounter a poetic sound device, write the example in the left column. Then, in the right column, explain the effect of the device, or how it enhances the text. The first passage has been done for you.*

Line or Phrase	Device	Effect
1. "Water, water, everywhere,/ Nor any drop to drink." ("Rime," lines 121–122)	repetition and alliteration	Repetition of the word *water* and of the *w* sound emphasizes the amount of water. Repetition of the *dr-* sound in *drop* and *drink* also emphasizes the lack of drinking water. The differing alliteration in each line contrats the amount of water with the lack of drinking water.
2.		
3.		
4.		
5.		

Name _____ Date _____

"The Rime of the Ancient Mariner" and **"Kubla Khan"** by Samuel Taylor Coleridge
Vocabulary Builder

Using the Root -*journ*-

A. DIRECTIONS: *Each of the following words contains the Latin root -*journ-*, which comes from the French and Latin words for "day." For each of the following sentences, choose one of the five words or phrases to replace the italicized word or phrase.*

adjourn	du jour	journal
journalism	journey	

1. The long day's *trip* had wiped me out completely. _____
2. I'm not so interested in writing fiction; I prefer *reporting*. _____
3. Kevin wrote all of his secret sorrows in his *diary*. _____
4. At midnight, the council finally decided that it was time for the meeting *to end for the day.*
   _____
5. Maggie ordered the radish salad and the soup *of the day*. _____

Using the Word List

averred	sojourn	expiated
reverence	sinuous	tumult

B. DIRECTIONS: *Choose the letter of the description that best fits each word below. Write the letters on the lines provided.*

___ 1. tumult
    A. commotion
    B. height
    C. depth
    D. gathering

___ 2. sinuous
    A. weak
    B. strong
    C. straight
    D. curving

___ 3. averred
    A. expressed ignorance
    B. stated to be true
    C. stated to be false
    D. defended weakly

___ 4. expiated
    A. breathed
    B. blamed
    C. explained
    D. atoned

___ 5. sojourn
    A. stay for a while
    B. visit briefly
    C. travel widely
    D. carry to

___ 6. reverence
    A. sadness
    B. veneration
    C. revisitation
    D. abhorrence

"The Rime of the Ancient Mariner" and **"Kubla Khan"** by Samuel Taylor Coleridge
Grammar and Style: Inverted Word Order

In standard English word order, the subject precedes the verb, the verb precedes the direct object, and a prepositional phrase follows the word it modifies. Sometimes a writer uses **inverted word order** to achieve a certain effect. The following lines from "Kubla Khan" provide an example.

Inverted word order: In Xanadu did Kubla Khan/A stately pleasure dome decree. . . .

Normal word order: Kubla Khan did decree a stately pleasure dome in Xanadu. . . .

A. PRACTICE: *For each of the following phrases, identify the sentence parts that have been inverted. Then rewrite the phrase or sentence, using normal word order.*

from "The Rime of the Ancient Mariner":

1. "At length did cross an Albatross. . . ."

_____

_____

2. "Instead of the cross, the Albatross/About my neck was hung."

_____

_____

from "Kubla Khan":

3. "Where was heard the mingled measure/From the fountain and the caves."

_____

_____

4. "A damsel with a dulcimer/In a vision once I saw. . . ."

_____

_____

B. Writing Application: *Rewrite each of these sentences using inverted word order.*

1. I saw a sprite in that light.

_____

2. His fingers wrapped around the pole; I knew that it would snap.

_____

3. The man and his dog ran up the walk to fetch the injured bird.

_____

4. Soft music slipped into my ears and sent me right to sleep.

_____

"The Rime of the Ancient Mariner" and **"Kubla Khan"** by Samuel Taylor Coleridge
Support for Writing

Use the cluster diagram to gather details from "The Rime of the Ancient Mariner" about the albatross and about its effects on the Mariner.

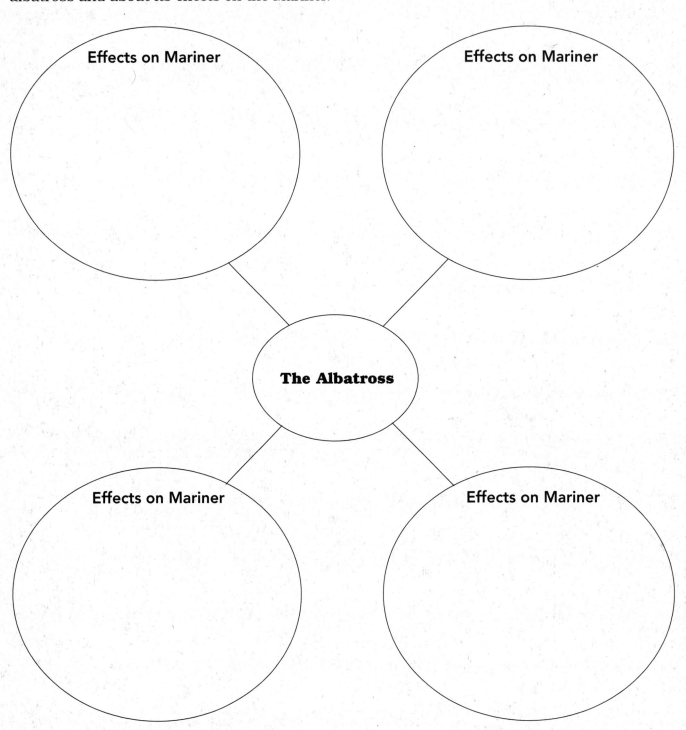

On a separate page, use the information you have gathered in your cluster diagram as you write your essay analyzing the meanings of the Albatross as a symbol.

"The Rime of the Ancient Mariner" and **"Kubla Khan"** by Samuel Taylor Coleridge
Support for Extend Your Learning

Listening and Speaking

Atmosphere is created by details in the setting that suggest a feeling or mood. Write details from your passage of "The Rime of the Ancient Mariner" that create mood. Then, use the details to draw a conclusion about the atmosphere that you will try to convey in your **dramatic reading.**

Detail:
Detail:
Conclusion about Atmosphere:

Research and Technology

Record your research in preparation for writing an **evaluation** of the literary friendship between Wordsworth and Coleridge. First, list bibliographic information. Then, list details you get from each source.

Bibliographic Information	Details about their literary friendship

Name _____ Date _____

"The Rime of the Ancient Mariner" and **"Kubla Khan"** by Samuel Taylor Coleridge
Enrichment: Science

Coleridge used dreams as the inspiration for both "The Rime of the Ancient Mariner" and "Kubla Khan." He claimed to have dreamt "Kubla Khan" word for word, after falling asleep while reading a passage about the real Kubla Khan, a figure in Chinese history. He modeled "The Rime of the Ancient Mariner" on a dream of his friend Mr. Cruikshank. In both poems Coleridge writes of fantastic events that have a dreamlike (or nightmarish) quality.

People have been fascinated by dreams for centuries and have developed many theories over the years about their cause and significance. Today, psychologists and biologists know that dreams occur during a stage of sleep called REM, or rapid eye movement, and some researchers believe that dreams are caused by random chemical stimuli in the brain. The brain tries to make sense of the activity, and the result is a dream. The meaning of dreams is a topic of controversy. Although dreams bear some relation to events and emotions that occur in waking hours, the nature of that relationship remains unclear.

A. DIRECTIONS: *Answer the following questions about the dreamlike elements in "The Rime of the Ancient Mariner" and "Kubla Khan."*

1. Review the poems and list at least five examples of dreamlike events or characters.

   _____

   _____

   _____

   _____

   _____

   _____

2. In "Kubla Khan," Coleridge refers to a particular dream. Identify that reference and explain its significance in the poem.

   _____

   _____

   _____

   _____

   _____

   _____

   _____

   _____

B. DIRECTIONS: *Find out more about dreams, using an encyclopedia, almanac, or the Internet. Choose one aspect of the scientific study of dreams, such how dream activity is recorded or how many times the average person dreams during eight hours of sleep. Compile the information in a short written report.*

"The Rime of the Ancient Mariner" and **"Kubla Khan"** by Samuel Taylor Coleridge
Selection Test A

Critical Reading *Identify the letter of the choice that best answers the question.*

____ 1. What does the ancient mariner in "The Rime of the Ancient Mariner" do that brings the curse on him?
A. He refuses to help his shipmates.
B. He sails into a forbidden part of the ocean.
C. He kills the albatross.
D. He interrupts the marriage ceremony.

____ 2. Which phrase from "The Rime of the Ancient Mariner" contains alliteration?
A. "And some in dreams . . ."
B. "The western wave was . . ."
C. "Had I from old . . ."
D. "A spring of love gushed . . ."

____ 3. Which of the following is one of the main themes of "The Rime of the Ancient Mariner"?
A. the value of all learning
B. the blessedness of all living things
C. the weakness of the human spirit
D. the importance of honesty

____ 4. What sound devices help emphasize the movement of the ship in "The Rime of the Ancient Mariner"?

Till noon we quietly sailed on,
Yet never a breeze did breathe;
Slowly and smoothly went the ship.
Moved onward from beneath.

A. The alliteration of the *b* and *s* sounds emphasizes the ship's gentle movement.
B. The assonance of the short *i* sound suggests the thirst of the mariner.
C. The internal rhyme of *slowly* and *smoothly* echoes the crushing waves.
D. The consonance of *yet* and *went* suggests the awfulness of the curse.

____ 5. In "The Rime of the Ancient Mariner," why does only the ancient mariner survive among the crew?
A. He clings to life because he knows supernatural powers will finally save the ship.
B. By killing the albatross, the ancient mariner gained supernatural strength to live.
C. He is the least guilty of them all for the death of the albatross.
D. As punishment for killing the albatross, he is condemned to live to tell the tale.

___ 6. Which line from "The Rime of the Ancient Mariner" contains an internal rhyme?

    A. "He struck with his o'ertaking wings"

    B. "And it grew wondrous cold"

    C. "That made the breeze to blow"

    D. "The ice did split with a thunder-fit"

___ 7. What is the tone of the "The Rime of the Ancient Mariner"?

    A. horror and awe

    B. fondness for a memory

    C. humor about one's faults

    D. relief and hope

___ 8. What is one of the central ideas of "Kubla Khan"?

    A. the power of the Chinese empire

    B. the vastness of the imagination

    C. life in the country

    D. the importance of rivers in poetry

___ 9. Which phrase from "Kubla Khan" contains assonance?

    A. "So twice five miles of fertile ground"

    B. "From the fountain and the caves"

    C. "A damsel and a dulcimer"

    D. "And drunk the milk of Paradise"

Vocabulary and Grammar

___ 10. Which sentence *incorrectly* uses the vocabulary word?

    A. The Ancient Mariner *averred* that he had killed the albatross.

    B. After his experience, the Ancient Mariner never *sojourned* for long in any place.

    C. The Ancient Mariner *expiated* his story to anyone who would listen.

    D. He had too little *reverence* for the power of nature.

___ 11. Which vocabulary word correctly completes this sentence?

    The winds and sea rose in _____ around the ship.

    A. tumult

    B. sojourn

    C. reverence

    D. expiation

___ **12.** Which answer choice shows an inverted word order that was used to create an effect?

    A. "It was a miracle of rare device."

    B. "A damsel with a dulcimer / In a vision once I saw . . ."

    C. "It was an Abyssinian maid . . ."

    D. "And there were gardens bright with sinuous rills . . ."

Essay

13. In "Kubla Khan," Coleridge describes a pleasure dome. In an essay, tell where it was, who built it, and what it was like. What was the most memorable or interesting image? Explain your response.

14. Think about the sound devices—alliteration, consonance, assonance, and internal rhyme—used by Coleridge in "The Rime of the Ancient Mariner." In an essay, tell how these devices contribute to the beauty and emotional impact of the poem. How did the devices make "The Rime of the Ancient Mariner" more than just a story? How did they contribute to how you feel about events and how you visualized them? Use at least two examples from the poem to support your response.

"The Rime of the Ancient Mariner" and "Kubla Khan" by Samuel Taylor Coleridge
Selection Test B

Critical Reading *Identify the letter of the choice that best completes the statement or answers the question.*

_____ 1. Which phrase from "The Rime of the Ancient Mariner" contains alliteration?
   A. "Was tyrannous and strong"
   B. "As green as emerald"
   C. "The ice was all around"
   D. "Hither to work us weal"

_____ 2. A central theme of "The Rime of the Ancient Mariner" is the
   A. sanctity of all wild creatures.
   B. goodness of all supernatural powers.
   C. equality of all human beings.
   D. excitement of all imaginative voyages.

_____ 3. Which line from "The Rime of the Ancient Mariner" contains alliteration, consonance, and internal rhyme?
   A. "At length did cross an Albatross . . ."
   B. "By thy long gray beard and glittering eye . . ."
   C. "In mist or cloud, on mast or shroud . . ."
   D. "The bride hath paced into the hall."

_____ 4. In which line are alliteration and variations on the *o* sound most evident, creating a heavy, grim tone?
   A. "And every tongue, through utter drought . . ."
   B. "And a good south wind sprung up behind . . ."
   C. "And the rain poured down from one black cloud . . ."
   D. "And the owlet whoops to the wolf below . . ."

_____ 5. Throughout his narration, the mariner maintains a tone of
   A. fresh horror and awe.
   B. pure relief and comfort.
   C. dull apathy and weariness.
   D. detached wonder and amusement.

_____ 6. The dice game between Death and Life-in-Death in "The Rime of the Ancient Mariner" suggests that
   A. sailors like to gamble.
   B. luck is all that matters.
   C. universal forces are not guided by reason.
   D. female forces are more powerful than male forces.

_____ 7. Which of these lines from "The Rime of the Ancient Mariner" contains internal rhyme?
   A. "Sweet sounds rose slowly through their mouths . . ."
   B. "They moved in tracks of shining white . . ."
   C. "Ah wretch! said they, the bird to slay . . ."
   D. "And listens like a three years' child . . ."

____ 8. Which is a favorite subject of the Romantics and is most evident in "Kubla Khan"?
   A. the classical and the mythological
   B. the moderate and the reasonable
   C. the faraway and the exotic
   D. the universal and the democratic

____ 9. What sound devices contribute to the poet's theme in lines like these?
   In Xanadu did Kubla Khan / A stately pleasure dome decree
   A. Blurring words create a vague, abstract feeling.
   B. Linking words create a flowing, dreamlike effect.
   C. Sharpening words create a precise, analytical tone.
   D. Separating words create a rigid, marchlike rhythm.

____ 10. In which line is alliteration the dominant sound device?
   A. "So twice five miles of fertile ground . . ."
   B. "A savage place! As holy and enchanted . . ."
   C. "Five miles meandering with a mazy motion . . ."
   D. "Through wood and dale the sacred river ran . . ."

____ 11. Which sound device helps to emphasize the largeness of the area of the grounds of the pleasure dome in these lines?
   So twice five miles of fertile ground
   With walls and towers were girdled round . . .
   A. alliteration—repetition of the *w* sound
   B. assonance—repetition of the long *i* sound
   C. consonance—repetition of the *s* sound
   D. consonance—repetition of the *d* sound

Vocabulary and Grammar

____ 12. Which word or phrase is closest in meaning to *adjourn*?
   A. end for the day
   B. cancel
   C. begin
   D. destroy

____ 13. The word *reverence* means _____.
   A. ministers
   B. hatred
   C. prayer
   D. respect

____ **14.** Which sentence most correctly rearranges the order of the inverted words from "The Rime of the Ancient Mariner"?

> O happy living things! no tongue
>
> Their beauty might declare . . .

A. O happy living things! your tongues might declare their beauty.

B. O happy living things! their beauty might declare no tongue.

C. O happy things living! no tongue their beauty might declare.

D. O happy living things! no tongue might declare their beauty.

____ **15.** Which sentence most correctly rearranges the order of the inverted words from "The Rime of the Ancient Mariner"?

> How long in that same fit I lay,
>
> I have not to declare . . .

A. I do not have to declare how long I lay in that same fit.

B. I have to declare how long I lay, not in that same fit.

C. I have not to declare how long I lay in that same fit.

D. I have to not declare how long I lay in that same fit.

Essay

16. In "Kubla Khan," Coleridge explores a fascination with exotic places and things. Write an essay analyzing his view and portrayal of Xanadu as an exotic place. Why do you think Coleridge is attracted to the exotic?

17. In "The Rime of the Ancient Mariner," the Polar Spirit's fellow demons describe him as follows: "The spirit who bideth by himself / In the land of mist and snow, / He loved the bird that loved the man / Who shot him with his bow." Write an essay analyzing the role that these lines play in "The Rime of the Ancient Mariner." Why are these lines important to the plot of the poem? What poetic effects does Coleridge use in these lines? What tone is created by the poetic effects in these lines?

Vocabulary Warm-up Word Lists

Study these words from the selections. Then, complete the activities that follow.

Word List A

ambition [am BISH uhn] *n.* the object or goal desired
  Joe's <u>ambition</u> is to become an actor.

conceal [kuhn SEEL] *v.* to hide
  Sam tried to <u>conceal</u> the present under his jacket.

express [ek SPRES] *v.* to convey; to communicate
  We are encouraged to <u>express</u> our opinions in class.

impaired [im PAYRD] *v.* lessened in strength or quality
  Because he was exposed to loud noises, Pat's hearing was <u>impaired</u>.

innocent [IN noh sent] *adj.* not guilty; blameless
  The jury concluded that the defendant was <u>innocent</u> of the charges brought against him.

praise [PRAYZ] *n.* a compliment; an expression of approval
  The artist earned <u>praise</u> for his skilled portrait of the woman.

squandered [SKWAHN duhrd] *v.* wasted
  Jeff <u>squandered</u> his money on candy and toys.

treasure [TREZH uhr] *n.* valuable or priceless possessions
  The pirate buried his <u>treasure</u> on the beach.

Word List B

aspect [AS pekt] *n.* the way a person or thing looks or is seen; facial expression
  His <u>aspect</u> showed that he was upset.

azure [AZH uhr] *adj.* the color blue
  The team's uniforms were <u>azure</u> and white.

bard [BAHRD] *v.* poet
  The <u>bard</u> recited his poetry before the crowd in the concert hall.

despise [des PYZ] *v.* to dislike intensely
  I <u>despise</u> dishonest people.

eloquent [EL oh kwent] *adj.* movingly expressive
  Paul's <u>eloquent</u> description of his best friend was very moving.

gaudy [GAW dee] *adj.* showy in a tasteless way
  Everyone wore <u>gaudy</u> costumes to the masquerade ball.

invincible [in VIN si buhl] *adj.* unbeatable; incapable of being overcome
  Sharon always wins her matches because she is <u>invincible</u>.

spurning [SPER ning] *v.* scorning; rejecting in an arrogant way
  <u>Spurning</u> a sincere offer of help is not a wise thing to do.

"She Walks in Beauty," *from* **Childe Harold's Pilgrimage** and *from* **Don Juan**
by George Gordon, Lord Byron
Vocabulary Warm-up Exercises

Exercise A *Fill the blanks, using each word from Word List A only once.*

Ever since he was a young boy, Robert's greatest [1] _____ was to become an opera singer. His most valuable [2] _____ was an old recording of the famous opera, "The Magic Flute." He loved to [3] _____ ideas through music. Robert never [4] _____ an opportunity to attend a live performance. Whenever someone gave him tickets to the opera, he made sure nothing [5] _____ his ability to attend it. He was also unable to [6] _____ his excitement, and he would shout for joy when he was given the tickets. Robert also took singing lessons and practiced regularly; the [7] _____ sound of his voice earned him a role as young boy in a local operatic production. He won great [8] _____ from music critics for his performance, and this led to future roles in other operas.

Exercise B *Decide whether each of the following statements is true or false. Circle* T *or* F, *and explain your answer.*

1. A <u>bard</u> works as a mechanical engineer.
   T / F _____

2. If your team has lost many games, it is <u>invincible</u>.
   T / F _____

3. Another word for the color blue is <u>azure</u>.
   T / F _____

4. You can sometimes tell how a person feels by examining their <u>aspect</u>.
   T / F _____

5. If you are wearing a <u>gaudy</u> outfit, you have on something elegant and tasteful.
   T / F _____

6. Poets are known for their <u>eloquent</u> expression of ordinary ideas.
   T / F _____

7. Some people <u>despise</u> the effects of pollution on our environment.
   T / F _____

8. The club's reputation for <u>spurning</u> applicants is widely known.
   T / F _____

"She Walks in Beauty," *from* **Childe Harold's Pilgrimage** and *from* **Don Juan**
by George Gordon, Lord Byron
Reading Warm-up A

Read the following passage. Pay special attention to the underlined words. Then, read it again, and complete the activities. Use a separate sheet of paper for your written answers.

George Gordon, Lord Byron, was a Romantic poet who owed much of his success to the circumstances of his life. As an <u>innocent</u> boy, Byron and his mother struggled to make ends meet. His father had <u>squandered</u> the family's money, and young Byron grew up in poverty. However, at the age of ten, Byron inherited wealth and title from an uncle, and from then on, his life became more comfortable. He went on to attend Cambridge University, where he published his first volume of poetry, *Hours of Idleness*. This book received no <u>praise</u>; in fact, it received almost universally bad reviews. Byron achieved real success with the publication of his second volume of poetry, *Childe Harold's Pilgrimage*, which was widely acclaimed.

Because he had the title of "lord," Byron was required to sit in the English Parliament, in the House of Lords. There, he was known for his ability to <u>express</u> his ideas well. Unfortunately, Byron's ability to communicate did not serve him well. His left-wing political beliefs <u>impaired</u> his success in Parliament, as many people there disagreed with his views. Because he could not <u>conceal</u> his political beliefs, and because he was in debt, Byron left England permanently and settled in Switzerland and later Italy. He would never set foot in England again.

Byron's time in Italy was a period of great creativity. He produced many famous works, including the literary <u>treasure</u> *Don Juan*.

Byron's real <u>ambition</u>, aside from writing poetry, was to help the underdog. This goal led him to Greece, where he had planned to fight with the Greeks and against the Turks, who controlled Greece at that time. Byron never attained this objective because he died of fever. He was buried in England, and is regarded as one of most important Romantic poets of that period.

1. Underline the phrase that tells what Byron and his mother had to struggle with while he was growing up as an <u>innocent</u> boy. Tell what *innocent* means.

2. Underline the phrase that tells the result that occurred after Byron's father <u>squandered</u> the family's money. Tell what *squandered* means.

3. Underline the phrase that supports the idea that Byron's first book received no <u>praise</u>. Tell what *praise* means.

4. Circle the word that tells what <u>express</u> means. Use *express* in a sentence.

5. Underline the phrase that explains how Byron's left-wing political views <u>impaired</u> his success in Parliament. Tell what *impaired* means.

6. Underline the phrase that tells what Byron had to do because he could not <u>conceal</u> his political beliefs. Tell what *conceal* means.

7. Circle the title of the literary <u>treasure</u> that Byron composed while he lived in Italy. Tell what *treasure* means.

8. Circle the word that tells what <u>ambition</u> means. Use *ambition* in a sentence.

Name _____ Date _____

"She Walks in Beauty," *from* **Childe Harold's Pilgrimage** and *from* **Don Juan**
by George Gordon, Lord Byron
Reading Warm-up B

Read the following passage. Pay special attention to the underlined words. Then, read it again, and complete the activities. Use a separate sheet of paper for your written answers.

George Gordon, Lord Byron, was almost as famous for his colorful personality as for his eloquent poetry. While he gracefully described the romance of the azure skies and unrequited love in his poetry, many people have viewed this bard as eccentric, unconventional, flamboyant, and controversial.

One important aspect of Byron's personality was his sympathy for victims. He was known to despise bullies, and as a student in school, he defended weaker students against them. It was this desire to defend the downtrodden that led Byron to Greece, where he had planned to fight in the war for independence against Turkey. Unfortunately, Byron was not invincible; he died before he had the opportunity to do so.

Furthermore, Byron did not follow the conventions of the times. Spurning the traditional political views of his contemporaries, he supported many liberal causes. He gained many political enemies because of these views, and he was forced to leave England partly as a result.

Byron was also quite fond of animals. Friends visiting his home have described it as a gaudy collection of a wide variety of pets, including monkeys, cats, peacocks, geese, a badger, a parrot, a heron, and his beloved dog, Boatswain.

The cult of Byron's personality can be equated with that of a modern rock star. As with such musicians, people flocked to the places where he recited his poetry. Even today, there is a Byron Society for people who are fascinated by his work. This society publishes a journal once a year in which Byron's work is analyzed and appreciated. Thirty-six such societies exist worldwide, and a conference about Byron and his work is held annually. Such activities serve to prove that, through his poetry and personality, Byron's effect on people has proved to be an enduring one.

1. In addition to his eloquent poetry, what else made Byron famous? Tell what *eloquent* means.

2. Underline the phrase that tells how people viewed Byron, even though he wrote graceful descriptions of the azure skies. Tell what *azure* means.

3. Underline the phrase that tells what the bard described in his poetry. Use *bard* in a sentence.

4. Underline the phrase that explains an important aspect of Byron's personality. Tell what *aspect* means.

5. Circle the word that tells who Byron was known to despise. Tell what *despise* means.

6. Why wasn't Byron invincible? Tell what *invincible* means.

7. Underline the phrase that explains what Byron did in spurning the traditional political views of his contemporaries. Tell what *spurning* means.

8. Underline the phrase that lists the gaudy collection of pets Byron kept. Tell what *gaudy* means.

Name _____ Date _____

"She Walks in Beauty," *from* **Childe Harold's Pilgrimage,**
and from **Don Juan** by George Gordon, Lord Byron
Literary Analysis: Figurative Language

To build powerful images, writers use **figurative language,** or figures of speech. Through figurative language, things that might at first seem completely unrelated are linked together.

Similes make comparisons using the word *like* or *as:*

The empty house was like a tomb.

Metaphors make comparisons without using *like* or *as:*

The empty house was a tomb.

Personification gives human characteristics to nonhuman subjects:

The empty house whispered of its past.

A. DIRECTIONS: *Following are passages from various poems. On the line at the right, identify the figure of speech that is used in each passage.*

1. "The lowered pulses of the river beat . . ." _____

2. "I tell you the past is a bucket of ashes." _____

3. The fields "were patched like one wide crazy quilt . . ." _____

4. ". . . drowsy lights along the paths/Are dim and pearled" _____

5. "The twigs are snapping like brittle bones." _____

B. DIRECTIONS: *Following is a series of items beside which are listed various types of figurative language. Describe each item in a sentence using the figure of speech indicated.*

1. storm clouds (personification) _____

_____

_____

2. courage (personification) _____

_____

_____

3. spring rain (simile) _____

_____

_____

4. the motorcycle (metaphor) _____

_____

_____

"She Walks in Beauty," *from* Childe Harold's Pilgrimage,
and *from* Don Juan by George Gordon, Lord Byron
Reading Strategy: Question

Poetry is meant to be read several times. You might read a poem once to get a general sense of its themes. On another reading, you might focus on the language and rhythm of the poem. Next you might pay special attention to its images. At least one of your readings should be devoted to achieving a basic understanding of what the poet is trying to communicate. You can do this by reading actively—asking questions about the poem and answering them. Ask questions that use the words *who, what, where, when,* and *why.* For example, consider the excerpt in your textbook from *Childe Harold's Pilgrimage:*

- **Question:** *What* does the speaker hope to communicate? **Answer:** He expresses admiration for the ocean.
- **Question:** *Why* does the speaker admire the ocean? **Answer:** Humans and human activities are insignificant in comparison to the ocean; the ocean is unchanging; it rules its domain and cannot be tamed by humans.

DIRECTIONS: *Read the excerpt in your textbook from* Don Juan. *Write questions about the poem using the words listed below. Then answer your questions.*

1. Who _____
   _____?
   _____
   _____

2. What _____
   _____?
   _____
   _____

3. What _____
   _____?
   _____
   _____

4. Why _____
   _____?
   _____
   _____

5. Why _____
   _____?
   _____
   _____

"She Walks in Beauty," *from* **Childe Harold's Pilgrimage,**
and *from* **Don Juan** by George Gordon, Lord Byron
Vocabulary Builder

Using the Suffix *-ous*

A. DIRECTIONS: *The following words all contain the suffix* -ous, *meaning "full of." In the blanks, complete each sentence with the appropriate word or words from the list.*

famous	delicious	miraculous	rebellious
ominous	adventurous	humorous	

1. The mushrooms tasted _____, but they were poisonous.

2. The _____ hero walked forward boldly into the storm, undeterred by the _____ lightning flashing all around him.

3. The politician was _____ for always beginning his speeches with a _____ anecdote.

4. Maude made a _____ recovery following cardiac surgery.

5. Feeling _____, Theo refused to celebrate the holidays.

Using the Word List

arbiter	credulous	retort	torrid	avarice
fathomless	tempests	copious	insensible	

B. DIRECTIONS: *Match each word in the left column with its definition in the right column. Write the letter of the definition on the line next to the word it defines.*

___ 1. retort   A. willing to believe

___ 2. credulous   B. numb

___ 3. copious   C. plentiful

___ 4. avarice   D. greed

___ 5. insensible   E. storms

___ 6. fathomless   F. reply with a wisecrack

___ 7. arbiter   G. too deep to measure

___ 8. tempests   H. very hot

___ 9. torrid   I. judge

"She Walks in Beauty," *from* **Childe Harold's Pilgrimage,**
and *from* **Don Juan** by George Gordon, Lord Byron

Grammar and Style: Subject and Verb Agreement

Every **verb** form that you write should agree in number with the noun that is its **subject.** A singular subject must have a singular verb, and a plural subject must have a plural verb.

Singular subject and verb:	*Time writes* no wrinkle on thine azure brow. . . .
	Where a *thought* serenely sweet *expresses*/How pure, how dear its dwelling place.
Plural subject and verb:	*Time and adversity write* no wrinkle on thine azure brow. . . . Where *thoughts* serenely sweet *express*/How pure, how dear their dwelling place.

A. PRACTICE: *Check each of the following sentences to see if its subject and verb agree in number. If they agree, write* agree *in the blank next to the sentence. If they do not agree, write the correct form of the verb in the blank next to the sentence. If there are two verbs, be sure to write the correct form of each in the blank.*

1. She *walks* in beauty, like the night. . . . _____

2. The smiles that win, the tints that glow, but *tells* of days in goodness spent . . .

   _____

3. There *are* a pleasure in the pathless woods. . . . _____

4. These *is* thy toys, and, as the snowy flake, / They *melts* into thy yeast of waves. . . .

   _____

5. their decay/*Have dried* up realms to deserts. . . . _____

6. *Roll* on, thou deep and dark blue ocean—*roll!* _____

B. Writing Application: *Write a sentence using each word or phrase below as the subject. Make sure that the verb agrees with the subject in each case.*

1. raindrop

   _____

2. dancer

   _____

3. coffee and tea

   _____

4. olives

   _____

5. strangers

   _____

Name _____ Date _____

"She Walks in Beauty," *from* Childe Harold's Pilgrimage, and *from* Don Juan by George Gordon, Lord Byron
Support for Writing

Use the chart below to gather and record ideas for your monologue.

Byronic Opinions that Fit Today's World	Byron's Circumstances and Attitude	Words and Phrases That Convey his Attitude

On a separate page, use the information you have gathered as you write your monologue.

Name _____   Date _____

"She Walks in Beauty," *from* **Childe Harold's Pilgrimage,**
and *from* **Don Juan** by George Gordon, Lord Byron
Support for Extend Your Learning

Research and Technology

Do research into the fashions, paintings, and lifestyles in England during the early 1800s, and record the details in the chart. Use the information for your **proposal for a portrait.**

	Details
Fashions	
Paintings	
Lifestyles	

Listening and Speaking

Use the organizer to collect ideas for your **eulogy.** Write details about Don Juan in the boxes on the left. Then, write conclusions you can draw about his character.

Details from the poem   **Conclusions about his character**

Name _____ Date _____

"She Walks in Beauty," *from* Childe Harold's Pilgrimage, and *from* Don Juan by George Gordon, Lord Byron
Enrichment: Film Portrayal of Don Juan

A traditional epic usually includes a larger-than-life hero—a brave figure who can accomplish deeds that would be impossible for the average person—and a great battle or a mission that must be accomplished. Often the hero travels to distant lands and overcomes many obstacles along the way.

Byron's *Don Juan* is a mock epic. Both the hero, Don Juan, and the narrator are ordinary and weak rather than extraordinary and strong. In this excerpt, the narrator makes fun of himself. He suggests that the things that mattered to him when he was younger—love affairs and poetic ambition—were a waste of time.

DIRECTIONS: *Use the graphic organizer below to develop a film treatment, or outline, for an epic movie about the life of the narrator of* Don Juan. *The movie should be organized as an epic, but like* Don Juan, *this epic should mock its hero rather than celebrate his exploits. Start with the biographical details mentioned by the narrator, but then use your imagination to elaborate on these details.*

	Plot	Location	Supporting Characters
Opening Scene			
The Narrator as a Young Man			
The Narrator at Age 30			
Closing Scence			

Name _____ Date _____

"She Walks in Beauty," *from* **Child Harold's Pilgrimage,** and *from* **Don Juan**
by George Gordon, Lord Byron
Selection Test A

Critical Reading *Identify the letter of the choice that best answers the question.*

____ 1. Which of the following is a central theme of "She Walks in Beauty"?
   A. goodness
   B. sorrow
   C. love
   D. bitterness

____ 2. Which question is answered by this line from "She Walks in Beauty"?
   She walks in beauty, like the night
   Of cloudless climes and starry skies;
   A. Which woman is the subject of the poem?
   B. Where is the woman going?
   C. Why is the woman so admired by the speaker?
   D. To what does the speaker compare the woman?

____ 3. Which line from *Child Harold's Pilgrimage* best answers this question: How does the speaker feel about nature?
   A. "Roll on, thou deep and dark blue ocean—roll!"
   B. "Thy shores are empires, changed in all save thee . . ."
   C. "I love not man the less, but nature more . . ."
   D. "What I can ne'er express, yet cannot all conceal."

____ 4. What is the main idea of *Child Harold's Pilgrimage*?
   A. People have built many civilizations.
   B. The ocean is unchanged by human activities.
   C. People use the ocean during war.
   D. Every generation finds reasons to fight wars.

____ 5. Which line from *Child Harold's Pilgrimage* includes a metaphor?
   A. "There is a pleasure in the pathless woods . . ."
   B. "Thou glorious mirror, where the Almighty's form / Glasses itself in tempests . . ."
   C. "Man marks the earth with ruin—his control / Stops with the shore . . ."
   D. "There is a rapture on the lonely shore . . ."

_____ 6. Which line from *Child Harold's Pilgrimage* is an example of personification?
A. "For earth's destruction thou [the ocean] dost all despise . . ."
B. "Man marks the earth with ruin—his control / Stops with the shore . . ."
C. "Monarchs tremble in their capitals . . ."
D. "An I have loved thee, ocean!"

_____ 7. What does the speaker in *Child Harold's Pilgrimage* say about civilizations?
A. They create great works of art.
B. They do not last over time.
C. They have a lasting effect on the world.
D. They have changed the ocean.

_____ 8. Which line from *Don Juan* contains a simile?
A. "The freshness of the heart can fall like dew . . ."
B. "I / Have spent my life, both interest and principal . . ."
C. "Ambition was my idol . . ."
D. "An flesh (which Death mows down to hay) is grass . . ."

_____ 9. Which words best describe the speaker in *Don Juan*?
A. serious and despairing
B. bold and aggressive
C. considerate and understanding
D. amusing and thoughtful

_____ 10. What is the speaker's point in telling about Cheops in *Don Juan*?
A. only fame matters
B. nothing lasts
C. great works of art last
D. fame is permanent

Vocabulary and Grammar

_____ 11. Which vocabulary word best completes this sentence?
As he grows older, the speaker in *Don Juan* is becoming _____ to love.
A. copious
B. credulous
C. insensible
D. torrid

_____ **12.** Which sentence uses a vocabulary word *incorrectly*?

    A. The speaker in *Child Harold's Pilgrimage* calls the ocean the *arbiter* of war.

    B. *Tempests* at sea threaten the mightiest ships.

    C. The speaker in *Don Juan* no longer has an interest in clever *retorts*.

    D. The speaker in "She Walks in Beauty" admires the lady's *avarice*.

_____ **13.** Which sentence shows *incorrect* subject and verb agreement?

    A. The speaker claims the monsters is formed from slime.

    B. The ocean is a source of wonder and beauty.

    C. The ocean remains untouched by the great civilizations.

    D. Ships that sail throughout the world do not change the ocean.

Essay

14. Think about the three poems: "She Walks in Beauty," the excerpt from *Child Harold's Pilgrimage,* and the excerpt from *Don Juan.* In an essay, compare their use of figurative language. Which poem uses the most figurative language? In which poem is the figurative language most memorable? Give examples of figurative language and reasons for your answer.

15. In the excerpt from *Don Juan,* the speaker thinks about his life. In an essay, tell how he has spent his life, and describe the conclusions that he has reached about life. What is his philosophy? Do you agree with it? Why or why not? Answer these questions in an essay. Give at least two examples to support your response.

"She Walks in Beauty," *from* **Childe Harold's Pilgrimage** and *from* **Don Juan**
by George Gordon, Lord Byron
Selection Test B

Critical Reading *Identify the letter of the choice that best completes the statement or answers the question.*

_____ 1. A central theme of "She Walks in Beauty" is the woman's _____.
A. joy
B. virtue
C. love
D. sorrow

_____ 2. Which line from "She Walks in Beauty" best answers the question "To what does the speaker compare the woman in the poem?"
A. "She walks in beauty, like the night . . ."
B. "Thus mellowed to that tender light . . ."
C. "How pure, how dear their dwelling place. . . ."
D. "But tell of days in goodness spent . . ."

_____ 3. Which pair of lines from "She Walks in Beauty" contains an example of personification?
A. "She walks in beauty, like the night / Of cloudless climes and starry skies . . ."
B. "And all that's best of dark and bright / Meet in her aspect and her eyes . . ."
C. "Where thoughts serenely sweet express / How pure, how dear their dwelling place."
D. "A mind at peace with all below, / A heart whose love is innocent!"

_____ 4. Why does the speaker of *Childe Harold's Pilgrimage* admire the ocean?
A. Many people depend on fish from the ocean for food.
B. The ocean is beautiful and its sounds are soothing.
C. The ocean provides a way to travel to faraway places.
D. The ocean is unchanged by human activities.

_____ 5. Which question is answered by the line from *Childe Harold's Pilgrimage*?
I love not man the less, but nature more
A. What is the theme of the poem?
B. Whom does the narrator love?
C. How does the narrator feel about nature?
D. Why do people rely on nature for sustenance?

_____ 6. Which of the lines from *Childe Harold's Pilgrimage* is an example of personification?
A. "And monarchs tremble in their capitals . . ."
B. ". . . thou dost arise / And shake him from thee . . ."
C. "And howling, to his gods, where haply lies / His petty hope . . ."
D. "Calm or convulsed—in breeze, or gale, or storm . . ."

_____ 7. A central theme of *Childe Harold's Pilgrimage* is the ocean's _____.
A. malice
B. permanence
C. rhythm
D. generosity

____ 8. A central idea of this excerpt from *Don Juan* is that the speaker's
   A. mind has increased its perception.
   B. heart has lost its power to feel.
   C. fame has dulled the dread of death.
   D. emotions have kept their intensity.

____ 9. To which question do these lines from *Don Juan* best provide an answer?
   My days of love are over; me no more
   The charms of maid, wife, and still less of widow
   Can make the fool of which they made before . . .

   A. When did the speaker pursue women?
   B. Why does the speaker avoid women?
   C. What was the speaker like when he was younger?
   D. What is the speaker like now?

____ 10. Which excerpt from *Don Juan* contains a metaphor?
   A. "Some liken it to climbing up a hill . . ."
   B. ". . . a chymic treasure / Is glittering youth . . ."
   C. "The freshness of the heart can fall like dew . . ."
   D. "Hived in our bosoms like the bag o' the bee . . ."

____ 11. At the end of the excerpt, the speaker appears to be trying to
   A. attack his critics.
   B. dismiss his peers.
   C. confess his sins.
   D. justify his book.

Vocabulary and Grammar

____ 12. Where thoughts serenely sweet _____ / How pure, how dear their dwelling place.
   A. has expressed
   B. was expressing
   C. express
   D. expresses

____ 13. There _____ a rapture on the lonely shore. . . .
   A. is
   B. are
   C. were
   D. be

____ 14. I / _____ squandered my whole summer while 'twas May. . . .
   A. Has
   B. Have
   C. Having
   D. To have

Name _____ Date _____

On the line, write the letter of the one best answer.

____ 15. The *arbiter* of war referred to by the speaker of *Childe Harold's Pilgrimage* could also be called
   A. the wager of war.
   B. the judge of war.
   C. the outcome of war.
   D. the winner of war.

____ 16. What does the speaker of *Don Juan* mean when he states that he no longer feels "the spirit to *retort*"?
   A. He thinks that he is not as spiritual as he used to be.
   B. He no longer feels driven to try to become famous.
   C. He does not feel the need to live his youth over again.
   D. He no longer feels able to respond with a wisecrack.

Essay

17. The word *apostrophe* can refer to words that are spoken to an object that is being personified. Write an essay explaining how the excerpt from *Childe Harold's Pilgrimage* is an "Apostrophe to the Ocean." How does the speaker compare the ocean to a person? According to the speaker, if the ocean were a person, what kind of person would the ocean be?

18. The speakers of "She Walks in Beauty" and "Apostrophe to the Ocean" express admiration for their subjects. But the speaker of *Don Juan* mocks his subject, which in this excerpt is himself. Write an essay contrasting the narrative styles of the three poems. How do the speakers of the first two poems use metaphors, similes, and personification to elevate their subjects? How does the speaker of *Don Juan* use these techniques to make fun of himself?

Vocabulary Warm-up Word Lists

Study these words from the selections. Then, complete the activities that follow.

Word List A

antique [an TEEK] *adj.* belonging to ancient times
    The antique platter was made during the Civil War.

decay [dee KAY] *n.* deterioration
    Many bacteria cause decay on the surfaces they touch.

hues [HYOOZ] *n.* colors
    A rainbow is made of many different hues.

keen [KEEN] *adj.* sharp; vivid
    Dogs have a keen sense of smell.

prophecy [PRAH feh see] *n.* a revelation; a prediction
    The oracle made a prophecy that the town would prosper.

scattering [SKAT uhr ing] *v.* dispersing; causing to break up and go in many places
    The wind blew in through the open window, scattering the papers on my desk.

solid [SAH lid] *adj.* not hollow; substantial
    That table is made of solid oak.

surpass [ser PAS] *v.* to outdo; to exceed
    We hoped that the trip would surpass our expectations.

Word List B

boyhood [BOY hood] *n.* a man's childhood
    My grandfather would tell us amusing stories of his boyhood.

commotion [kuhm MOH shuhn] *n.* agitation; disorder
    The fight caused a commotion in the hotel lobby.

colossal [cuhl LAH sul] *adj.* gigantic; huge
    The Sears Tower in Chicago is a colossal skyscraper.

dirge [DERJ] *n.* a funeral hymn
    The chorus sang a dirge at the man's funeral.

sculptor [SKULP tuhr] *n.* one who creates three-dimensional designs
    The sculptor displayed his series of lifelike figures in clay at the museum.

tumult [TUM uhlt] *n.* a great disturbance
    The tumult of the crowd was caused by a loud explosion.

visage [VIS ej] *n.* a person's face or appearance
    After the telephone call, her visage was marked by a frown.

wanderings [WAHN duhr ingz] *n.* acts of roaming about; meanderings
    The traveler's wanderings led him to faraway and exotic places.

"Ozymandias," "Ode to the West Wind," and **"To a Skylark"** by Percy Bysshe Shelley
Vocabulary Warm-up Exercises

Exercise A *Fill in each blank using each word from Word List A only once.*

Though the [1] _____ quilt was probably over one hundred years old, it was unfaded. You could appreciate the bright [2] _____ of the individual squares today because of the way it had been stored. The trunk that held the quilt for all these years was made of [3] _____ maple, so no light or dust had penetrated. The quilt experts who examined it used their [4] _____ knowledge of fabrics and textiles quilt to determine its value. They were very pleased that the original owner had kept the quilt intact instead of [5] _____ pieces to flea markets across the country. They also found no evidence of [6] _____ on either side. Many of these experts thought that the price it would bring at auction would [7] _____ quilts sold recently. One expert was so enthusiastic about the quilt's condition that he made a [8] _____ that a museum, not an individual collector, would be the buyer.

Exercise B *Decide whether each statement below is true or false. Circle* T *or* F, *and explain your answer.*

1. If something is <u>colossal</u>, it is very small.
   T / F _____

2. A <u>commotion</u> can occur during a football game.
   T / F _____

3. A <u>dirge</u> is played during sports events.
   T / F _____

4. Your <u>visage</u> can reveal your feelings even if you say nothing.
   T / F _____

5. A <u>sculptor</u> works with watercolors.
   T / F _____

6. A <u>tumult</u> is usually a very quiet event.
   T / F _____

7. You can discover new and interesting things during <u>wanderings</u> in an unfamiliar place.
   T / F _____

8. Some male athletes began playing sports during their <u>boyhood</u>.
   T / F _____

"Ozymandias," "Ode to the West Wind," and **"To a Skylark"** by Percy Bysshe Shelley

Reading Warm-up A

Read the following passage. Pay special attention to the underlined words. Then, read it again, and complete the activities. Use a separate sheet of paper for your written answers.

Percy Bysshe Shelley considered the politically conservative climate of the England in which he was raised an antique holdover from earlier times. He believed it was this political conservatism that was directly responsible for inequality among the classes. These views are expressed in his poetry and in his many essays and articles.

As a young boy, Shelley had few friends, and he was taunted by other students. Perhaps, because of these experiences, it wouldn't be hard to make the prophecy that Shelley would develop a strong dislike of tyranny. His keen objections to it are reflected in his writing.

Shelley met influential politicians and read about important issues. This gave him a solid foundation in politics. He was expelled from college when it was discovered that he wrote pamphlet about atheism. After this, Shelley married Harriet Westhook, and they traveled throughout England and Ireland, speaking against political injustice and scattering pamphlets about the subject wherever they went.

He also wrote many articles regarding his views about the decay and deterioration of English society.

After his first marriage ended, Shelley met and married Mary Wollstonecraft Godwin, a fellow writer. Their travels and life abroad together inspired him to write some of his most famous works. While in Italy, Shelley published the political magazine *The Liberal* with his friends, Lord Byron and Leigh Hunt.

One of Shelley's beliefs was that people of all social hues should be permitted to participate in political life—in other words, everyone should have a voice. He wrote an article suggesting a national discussion on reforming the election process and improving the educational system for the working class.

Although Shelley drowned when he was only twenty-five, it was clear that he had already developed a body of work that would surpass many of his writer contemporaries for its beauty, style, and content.

1. What did Shelley consider an antique holdover from earlier times? Then, write a sentence using the word *antique*.

2. Underline the phrase that tells what prophecy one could make about Shelley. What would your *prophecy* about Shelley be?

3. Underline the phrase that explains where Shelley's keen objections can be found. Define what *keen* means.

4. Underline the sentence that reveals how Shelley received his solid foundation in radical politics. How might a person without a *solid* political foundation act.

5. Underline the phrase that explains where Shelley and his wife were scattering pamphlets. Can politicians be found *scattering* pamphlets? Explain.

6. Circle the word that tells what decay means. Use *decay* in a sentence.

7. Underline Shelley's belief about people of all social hues. Define *hues*.

8. Underline the phrase that explains what Shelley's work would surpass. Describe a goal that an athlete might like to *surpass*?

"Ozymandias," "Ode to the West Wind," and **"To a Skylark"** by Percy Bysshe Shelley

Reading Warm-up B

Read the following passage. Pay special attention to the underlined words. Then, read it again, and complete the activities. Use a separate sheet of paper for your written answers.

Percy Bysshe Shelley achieved <u>colossal</u> fame as a Romantic poet because of his inate talent, and in part, due to the efforts of his wife, Mary Wollstonecraft Shelley, to enhance and preserve his literary reputation. While their relationship at times caused a <u>commotion</u>, the two shared a bond created by their love of literature and the arts.

Shelley first encountered Mary during a meeting with her father, a well-known political radical and free thinker, a point of view Shelley had adopted during his unhappy <u>boyhood</u>. The couple eventually eloped and traveled throughout Europe. After their <u>wanderings</u>, they returned to England, where they discovered that their elopement had caused a great <u>tumult</u>, particularly with Mary's father, who initially disapproved of the match.

Yet the Shelleys' relationship proved fruitful. Shelley regarded Mary as someone who experienced and understood poetry and philosophy on the same level as he did.

Like her husband, Mary was a <u>sculptor</u> of words. The two created worlds of fiction and poetry—carefully, as though molding clay. Mary wrote her famous novel *Frankenstein* after the couple attended a party at Lord Byron's villa on Lake Geneva, Switzerland, the summer of 1816. During a terrible storm, Byron challenged his guests to write ghost stories, and Mary got her ideas for her novel when the group discussed their work. *Frankenstein* was published two years later.

News of Shelley's drowning death saddened his friends, who gathered for a ceremony on a beach to honor him. Organized by Byron, Shelley's funeral was untraditional and did not include a <u>dirge</u>.

After her husband's death, Mary continued her own writing. Her tireless dedication to preserving and promoting Shelley's work helped cement his reputation. To this day, though people may not recognize Shelley's expressive <u>visage</u> from likenesses, they do recognize and appreciate his words.

1. Underline why Shelley achieved <u>colossal</u> fame. Write a sentence using the word *colossal*.

2. Circle what caused a <u>commotion</u>. Then, use *commotion* in a sentence.

3. What similarity did Shelley share with Mary's father since his <u>boyhood</u>? Describe what Shelley's political leanings might be if his *boyhood* had been happy.

4. Underline the phrase that tells where Shelley and Mary went in their <u>wanderings</u>. Rewrite the sentence using a synonym of *wanderings*.

5. Circle the word that tells what caused a <u>tumult</u> upon their return from Europe. Define *tumult*?

6. Underline the phrase that explains how Mary, like Shelley, was also a <u>sculptor</u>. Rewrite the sentence using a synonym of *sculptor*.

7. Underline the words that reveal why there was no <u>dirge</u> at Shelley's funeral.

8. Underline the phrase that tells why Shelley is still popular, even though his <u>visage</u> may not be familiar. Rewrite the sentence using a synonym of *visage*.

"Ozymandias," "Ode to the West Wind," and "To a Skylark"
by Percy Bysshe Shelley
Literary Analysis: Imagery

Poets use vivid **imagery** for many reasons. Appealing to a reader's senses of sight, hearing, taste, smell, and touch can make the poem seem more real to the reader. Certain images may also inspire a reader to respond with feelings of awe, disgust, fear, desire, amusement, or joy, to name just a few. But poets do not use images purely to keep the reader's interest—often, the images in a poem help to develop the poem's theme. For example, in "To a Skylark," Shelley uses imagery to reinforce the theme of creativity. He compares the bird to the moon, a poet, a highborn maiden, a glowworm, and a rose. The subject of each image emits or creates a beautiful thing: The moon and glowworm both emit light, the poet creates poetry, the maiden sings, and the rose emits a pleasant odor.

DIRECTIONS: *Answer the following questions on the lines provided.*

> . . . Two vast and trunkless legs of stone
> Stand in the desert. Near them, on the sand,
> Half sunk, a shattered visage lies, whose frown,
> And wrinkled lip, and sneer of cold command . . .
> ("Ozymandias," lines 2–5)

1. To what senses does this image appeal?

   _____

2. What emotions might this image provoke in a reader?

   _____

3. To what senses does this image appeal?

   _____

4. What emotions might this image provoke in a reader?

   _____

5. How is this image related to the theme of the poem?

   _____

   _____

"Ozymandias," "Ode to the West Wind," and **"To a Skylark"**
by Percy Bysshe Shelley

Reading Strategy: Respond to Imagery

Poets use descriptive language, or **imagery,** to make their writing seem more real and vivid to the reader. They do this by appealing to a reader's physical senses with visual details, sounds, smells, tastes, and textures. In order to **respond to a poem's imagery,** you must use your imagination and draw on your life experience. For example, you might respond to Shelley's mention of rain by imagining what rain feels like against your skin.

DIRECTIONS: *As you read these poems, copy several passages that contain vivid images in the first column of the graphic organizer below. In the second column, describe the image in your own words. Include details that Shelley implies but may not specifically mention. Remember to include sounds, smells, tastes, and textures, as well as sights, if appropriate. In the third column list the senses (sight, hearing, touch, smell, or taste) through which the image can be experienced.*

Passage	Description of Image	Senses
1. "Round the decay / Of that colossal wreck, boundless and bare, / The lone and level sands stretch far away." ("Ozymandias," lines 12–14)	The statue is surrounded by a vast empty desert where it is dry and hot and there is no sound but the wind.	sight, touch, sound
2.		
3.		
4.		
5.		

Name _____ Date _____

"Ozymandias," "Ode to the West Wind," and "To a Skylark"
by Percy Bysshe Shelley
Vocabulary Builder

Using the Root -puls-

A. DIRECTIONS: *The word root -puls- means "push" or "drive." Using your knowledge of the word root -puls- and the information in parentheses, replace each italicized word or phrase with a word that includes the word root -puls-. Write the new word on the line that follows the sentence.*

compulsive (*com-* = with)	repulse (*re-* = against)
pulsar (*-ar* = of or relating to)	impulsiveness (*im-* = toward)

1. Astronomers began to pick up waves of electromagnetic radiation that were being emitted from a previously unknown *neutron star.* _____

2. Because he is *a/an obsessive* shopper, Isaiah can't save money. _____

3. Maddie regretted her *spontaneity* after she threw her book out the window. _____

4. The army used tanks to *drive back* the attacking forces. _____

Using the Word List

visage	verge	sepulcher	impulse
blithe	profuse	vernal	satiety

B. DIRECTIONS: *Fill in each blank with a word from the Word List.*

1. Mary visited the graveyard to put flowers by her ancestor's _____.

2. It was difficult to stop the flooding because the flow of water was so _____

3. The _____ equinox signals the first day of spring.

4. Don't ever show your sorry _____ around here again!

5. After the pie-eating contest, Harold was beyond _____; he was on the _____ of being sick.

6. José loved his grandmother, but her _____ response to even the most depressing events irritated him.

7. When the rescue ship sailed into the harbor and unloaded the survivors, Sarah obeyed her sudden _____ to kneel and kiss the solid ground.

Name _____ Date _____

"Ozymandias," "Ode to the West Wind," and "To a Skylark"
by Percy Bysshe Shelley
Grammar and Style: Subjunctive Mood

The **subjunctive mood** is used to refer to possible rather than actual actions. For example, writers use the subjunctive mood to suggest that something might happen, express doubt that something will happen, voice a desire for something to happen, or note that if one action occurs another is likely to follow. The subjunctive can be formed with the plural past tense of the verb *to be (were)* or with helping verbs like *could, would,* or *should.*

Subjunctive:

The skylark could fly away.

The skylark should fly away.

I insist that the skylark fly away.

The skylark would fall out of the sky,

   were it not to spread its wings and fly.

Not subjunctive:

The skylark will fly away.

The skylark is flying away.

The skylark flew away.

The skylark has flown away,

A. PRACTICE: *Underline the subjunctive verbs in the following verses from "Ode to the West Wind."*

If I were a dead leaf thou mightest bear;
If I were a swift cloud to fly with thee;
A wave to pant beneath thy power, and share
The impulse of thy strength, only less free
Than thou, O uncontrollable! If even
I were as in my boyhood, and could be
The comrade of thy wanderings over Heaven,
As then, when to outstrip thy skyey speed
Scarce seemed a vision; I would ne'er have striven
As thus with thee in prayer in my sore need.

B. Writing Application: *Rewrite each of the following sentences, changing the verb form to the subjunctive. Be sure to change the rest of the sentence too, if necessary.*

1. That apple cannot fall far from the tree.

   _____

2. Samantha will hurt herself when she loses her balance on those slippery steps.

   _____

3. I am sorry you are not happy about this decision.

   _____

4. Marty refused to resign from the company.

   _____

5. Bruno is not able to talk, even though he may want to—he's only a dog.

   _____

"Ozymandias," "Ode to the West Wind," and **"To a Skylark"**
by Percy Bysshe Shelley
Support for Writing

Use the lines below to record questions and to organize your research into the scientific and historical background of one of Shelley's poems.

1. Specific question: _____

   _____

   A. General question: _____

   _____

   B. General question: _____

   _____

2. Specific question: _____

   _____

   A. General question: _____

   _____

   B. General question: _____

   _____

3. Specific question: _____

   _____

   A. General question: _____

   _____

   B. General question: _____

   _____

Use your questions to guide your research into the background of your poem. On a separate page, use the information you gather to support your introduction.

"Ozymandias," "Ode to the West Wind," and **"To a Skylark"**
by Percy Bysshe Shelley

Support for Extend Your Learning

Listening and Speaking

Use a thesaurus, the Internet, or other references to identify technical language describing wind. Write the definitions and then write a sentence using the term to apply to the west wind. Use the terms in your **weather report.**

Technical Term: _____	Definition: _____
	Informal sentence about the west wind: _____ _____
Technical Term: _____	Definition: _____
	Informal sentence about the west wind: _____ _____
Technical Term: _____	Definition: _____
	Informal sentence about the west wind: _____ _____

Research and Technology

Use the following organizer to develop ideas for your **cultural report** about Constable's art, one of his paintings, and how they are linked to Romantic poetry.

Details about Constable's art　　　　　　　　　**Details about Romantic poetry**

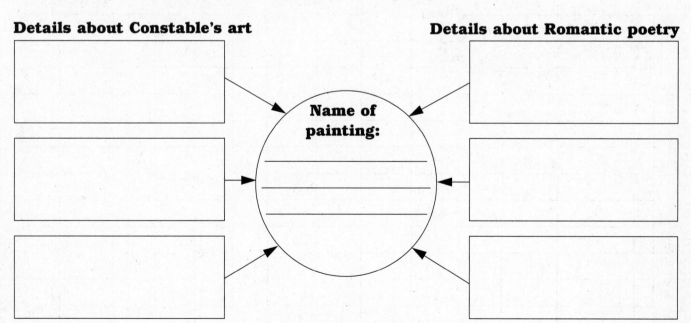

"Ozymandias," "Ode to the West Wind," and **"To a Skylark"**
by Percy Bysshe Shelley
Enrichment: Meteorology

The Romantic poets had something in common with modern meteorologists, who study the atmosphere, weather, and climate. Both observed nature carefully, and Shelley even had some scientific training. However, while poets like Shelley romanticized nature—personifying it and describing it with metaphors and similes—meteorologists demystify nature and try to predict what it will do. The Romantic poets relied on the evidence of their senses, while meteorologists rely on tools such as weather satellites, thermometers, barometers, weather balloons, and computers.

There are a number of careers in meteorology. For example, *operational meteorologists* gather and interpret current data to forecast the weather; *climatologists* compile and study records of past weather conditions to understand long-term weather patterns; *physical meteorologists* study the atmosphere itself; and *dynamic meteorologists* study the physical laws of air currents to understand the motions of weather systems.

DIRECTIONS: *Select one of the meteorological specialties above. Use the careers section of the library's reference department or the Internet to discover the educational and technical requirements for a position in this field, as well as possible employers, such as the military, a metropolitan airport, or an environmental organization. Record your information on the lines provided. Then use your notes to prepare a short oral report to the class.*

_____

_____

_____

_____

_____

_____

_____

_____

_____

_____

_____

_____

_____

_____

_____

_____

Unit 4 Resources: Rebels and Dreamers

"Ozymandias," "Ode to the West Wind," and **"To a Skylark"** by Percy Bysshe Shelley

Selection Test A

Critical Reading *Identify the letter of the choice that best answers the question.*

____ 1. What is the main idea of "Ozymandias"?
   A. Power and fame are short-lived.
   B. The desert is vast and lonely.
   C. Ozymandias was a great king.
   D. Travelers see and know many things.

____ 2. Which word best describes King Ozymandias?
   A. generous
   B. foolish
   C. proud
   D. old

____ 3. Which line from "Ozymandias" best states the poem's theme?
   A. "I met a traveler from an antique land"
   B. "Its sculptor well those passions read / Which yet survive . . ."
   C. "Two vast and trunkless legs of stone/ Stand in the desert."
   D. "Look on my works, ye Mighty, and despair!"

____ 4. What senses are appealed to in this image from "Ode to the West Wind"?
   Thine azure sister of the Spring shall blow
   Her clarion o'er the dreaming earth, and fill . . .
   With loving hues and odors plain and hill:
   A. taste, touch, sound
   B. sight, sound, smell
   C. sight, sound, touch
   D. sight, taste, touch

____ 5. Which image from "Ode to the West Wind" best expresses the speaker's hopes?
   A. "And saw in sleep old palaces and towers . . ."
   B. "know / Thy voice, and suddenly grow gray with fear . . ."
   C. "I fall upon the thorns of life! I bleed!"
   D. "Make me thy lyre, even as the forest is. . . ."

_____ 6. Which statement is the best translation of this image from "Ode to the West Wind"?

> Drive my dead thought over the universe
> Like withered leaves to quicken a new birth!

   A. If my poems are scattered everywhere, they will inspire new ideas.

   B. Words that express dead ideas serve no lasting purpose.

   C. My poems have been read in many places around the world.

   D. I do not care if people read my poems; creating them is all that matters.

_____ 7. How is the image of the wind in "Ode to the West Wind" like the image of the skylark in "To a Skylark"?

   A. Both are cold and threatening.

   B. Both are always moving.

   C. Both are cheerful.

   D. Both suggest endings.

_____ 8. In "To a Skylark," what does the speaker say is the skylark's greatest quality?

   A. the purity of its joy

   B. the intensity of its feelings

   C. the speed of its flight

   D. the loudness of its song

_____ 9. How is human joy different from the skylark's joy in "To a Skylark"?

   A. A skylark's joy is based on unlimited freedom.

   B. A skylark has joy only when flying.

   C. Human joy is always touched by sorrow.

   D. Human joy is not heard by others.

Vocabulary and Grammar

_____ 10. Which vocabulary word correctly completes this sentence?

> The _____ of the statue showed the facial expression of someone who was accustomed to being obeyed.

   A. impulse

   B. sepulcher

   C. verge

   D. visage

___ **11.** Which word best describes the song of the skylark in "To a Skylark"?

    A. blithe

    B. vernal

    C. satiety

    D. impulsive

___ **12.** Which phrase uses the subjunctive mood?

    A. "The winged seeds, where they lie cold and low . . ."

    B. "Will be the dome of a vast sepulcher. . . ."

    C. "If I were a swift cloud to fly with thee . . ."

    D. "Oh, lift me as a wave, a leaf, a cloud!"

Essay

13. In an essay, explain the main message of "Ozymandias." Give at least two examples from the poem that explain how the images support the message.

14. One of the main characteristics of the Romantic poets was the close connections they saw between humans and nature. The images in Shelley's poems make particularly powerful connections between Shelley's own spirit and nature. Write an essay describing how Shelley makes this connection in "To a Skylark." Point out some images he uses to make this comparison.

"Ozymandias," "Ode to the West Wind," and **"To a Skylark"** by Percy Bysshe Shelley
Selection Test B

Critical Reading *Identify the letter of the choice that best completes the statement or answers the question.*

_____ 1. One of the most important ideas of "Ozymandias" is the
   A. permanence of sculpted monuments.
   B. insignificance of physical death.
   C. meaninglessness of earthly power.
   D. poetry of glorious inscriptions.

_____ 2. Which sentence best explains who Ozymandias was?
   A. He was a king of Egypt during Shelley's time.
   B. He was a king of Egypt thousands of years before Shelley wrote.
   C. He was a traveler who discovered the king's statue.
   D. He was the speaker of the poem "Ozymandias."

_____ 3. In "Ozymandias," Shelley describes only what the traveler saw. What else might the traveler have experienced while looking at the statue?
   A. the singing of birds
   B. the heat of the sun
   C. the taste of fresh water
   D. the smell of cooking food

_____ 4. What do you think is the political message of "Ozymandias"?
   A. No dictator can ever truly rule absolutely.
   B. It is better to live without any kind of government.
   C. People should rule their country democratically.
   D. Those who rule should do so with kindness and compassion.

_____ 5. The descriptions of the West Wind in the first two sections of "Ode to the West Wind" are dominated by images of
   A. violence, death, decay, and burial.
   B. sleep, dreams, fantasy, and reverie.
   C. peace, birth, growth, and blossoming.
   D. translucence, light, color, and radiance.

_____ 6. Which statement best summarizes Shelley's depiction of the West Wind?
   A. The West Wind represents the goodness of nature.
   B. The West Wind represents the destructive power of nature.
   C. The West Wind's destructiveness makes new life possible.
   D. The West Wind brings the spring.

_____ 7. Which image best expresses the speaker's hopes for the West Wind?
   A. "Scatter, as from an extinguished hearth / Ashes and sparks . . ."
   B. "Make me thy lyre, even as the forest is . . ."
   C. ". . . he lay, / Lulled by the coil of his crystalline streams . . ."
   D. "If I were a dead leaf thou mightest bear . . ."

____ 8. What images do the lines from "Ode to the West Wind" suggest?

> Loose clouds like earth's decaying leaves are shed, / Shook from the tangled boughs of Heaven and Ocean . . .

A. Heaven and Ocean are like large trees.
B. Clouds ascend to Heaven from earth.
C. Clouds fall to earth after they decay.
D. Heaven and Ocean are connected by trees.

____ 9. In "To a Skylark," what quality does Shelley perceive and praise above all in the skylark's existence?

A. the poignancy and melancholy of its song
B. the clarity and wisdom of its understanding
C. the purity and simplicity of its joy
D. the variety and intensity of its emotions

____ 10. Which image from "To a Skylark" suggests that the skylark's music is everywhere at once?

A. "The pale purple even / Melts around thy flight . . ."
B. "As from thy presence showers a rain of melody."
C. "Like a glowworm golden / In a dell of dew . . ."
D. "Like a rose embowered / In its own green leaves . . ."

____ 11. According to the speaker of "To a Skylark," how is human happiness different from the skylark's happiness?

A. The skylark does not know that it will die one day.
B. Humans know too much to experience the skylark's simple joy.
C. Humans cannot know the joy of flying.
D. Human happiness is always tinged with sorrow.

____ 12. Which statement best describes the overall image of the skylark presented in "To a Skylark"?

A. The skylark is often invisible.
B. The skylark appears everywhere.
C. The skylark is bright and colorful.
D. The skylark is gray and drab.

____ 13. Which statement best describes Shelley's depiction of nature in "Ozymandias," "Ode to the West Wind," and "To a Skylark"?

A. Nature has much to teach us.
B. Nature is destructive but beautiful.
C. Nature should be protected and preserved.
D. Nature should be admired for its delicate beauty.

____ 14. How is the image Shelley draws of the wind in "Ode to the West Wind" similar to the image he creates of the skylark in "To a Skylark"?

A. Both are bright and cheerful.
B. Both are visible only at certain times of the year.
C. Both are constantly in motion.
D. Both are startling and fearsome.

Vocabulary and Grammar

____ 15. What does Shelley mean by these words in "Ode to the West Wind"?

this closing night / Will be the dome of a vast *sepulcher*

    A. The night is like a womb.
    B. The night is like a tomb.
    C. The night is like a church.
    D. The night is like a storm.

____ 16. Which phrase from "Ode to the West Wind" is written in the subjunctive mood?
    A. "Angels of rain and lightning: there are spread . . ."
    B. "Black rain, and fire, and hail will burst: oh, hear!"
    C. "If I were a swift cloud to fly with thee . . ."
    D. "Oh, lift me as a wave, a leaf, a cloud!"

Essay

17. At the end of "Ode to the West Wind," the speaker asks the wind, "If Winter comes, can Spring be far behind?" Write an essay in which you interpret the meaning of this question. How does this question help to explain why the speaker admires the West Wind so much? Read in the light of this passage, what does "Ode to the West Wind" suggest about Shelley's attitude toward death? Use examples from the poem to support your answer.

18. The speaker of "Ode to the West Wind" speaks not only of the wind, but of himself. Write an essay explaining what the speaker hopes to gain from his relationship with the West Wind. Why does he address the wind? What problem is disturbing the speaker? Use examples from the poem to support your answer.

Vocabulary Warm-up Word Lists

Study these words from the selections. Then, complete the activities that follow.

Word List A

brim [BRIM] *n.* the rim of a vessel; edge
The <u>brim</u> that man's hat is a small one.

dissolve [diz ZAHLV] *v.* melt; disintegrate
Those tablets will <u>dissolve</u> in water.

fame [FAYM] *n.* great renown
The artist's <u>fame</u> made him well-known to everyone.

immortal [im MOHR tuhl] *adj.* lasting forever; not subject to death
In ancient mythology, the gods were described as <u>immortal</u>.

passion [PASH uhn] *n.* boundless enthusiasm; zeal
John's great <u>passion</u> for cooking led to his career as a chef.

pursuit [per SOOT] *n.* an activity, such as a hobby or vocation
My favorite <u>pursuit</u> is reading.

realms [RELMZ] *n.* areas; domains
The social sciences cover many different <u>realms</u> of study.

rhyme [RIME] *n.* the correspondence of sounds at the ends of words
Jack composed a <u>rhyme</u> with very common words.

Word List B

abroad [uh BRAWD] *adv.* in a foreign country
We traveled <u>abroad</u> to Spain for our vacation.

attitude [AT ti tewd] *n.* disposition; one's state of mind
Cheryl has a cheerful <u>attitude</u> toward life.

cease [SEES] *v.* discontinue; stop
We will not <u>cease</u> in our rescue efforts until we have saved all of the victims.

forlorn [fohr LOHRN] *adj.* lonely because of abandonment
The <u>forlorn</u> puppy barked for its mother.

legend [LEJ uhnd] *n.* an unverified popular story that is handed down
There is a well-known <u>legend</u> about the area the family lives in.

lustrous [LUS trus] *adj.* having a glow or sheen; radiant
The <u>lustrous</u> pearls glowed in the sunshine.

perilous [PER i lus] *adj.* dangerous
Riding a bicycle without a helmet is a <u>perilous</u> activity.

relish [REL ish] *v.* to enjoy; to take pleasure in
I <u>relish</u> working in my garden because it gives me great joy.

Selected Poetry of John Keats
Vocabulary Warm-up Exercises

Exercise A *Fill in the blanks, using each word from Word List A only once.*

A poet deals with more than just rhythm and [1] _____ when she writes

poetry. She is in [2] _____ of much more than that. A poet also deals with

various [3] _____ of fiction and reality when she decides on the content of

the poem. She works to make the lines between those two worlds [4] _____

so that all that remains is the picture that she paints with her words. A good poem is

filled to the [5] _____ with rich language, sounds, and images. It is the

product of a writer who has a [6] _____ for words and how to use them to

create beauty. A good poem can also bring the poet [7] _____ because

everyone will want to read it. However, a truly great poem can make the poet

[8] _____ because it will endure the test of time.

Exercise B *Decide whether each of the following statements is true or false. Circle* T *or* F, *and explain your answer.*

1. If you <u>cease</u> to do something, you have just begun it.

_____

2. A <u>legend</u> is a true story.

_____

3. Climbing a mountain without adequate safety equipment can be <u>perilous</u>.

_____

4. An example of a place that is located <u>abroad</u> is Cairo, Egypt.

_____

5. A person would usually <u>relish</u> doing something she enjoys.

_____

6. Velvet is a <u>lustrous</u> fabric.

_____

7. You need to have a positive <u>attitude</u> when you are preparing to do a difficult task.

_____

8. If you are <u>forlorn</u>, you are surrounded by your friends.

_____

Name _____ Date _____

Selected Poetry of John Keats
Reading Warm-up A

Read the following passage. Pay special attention to the underlined words. Then, read it again, and complete the activities. Use a separate sheet of paper for your written answers.

John Keats did not gain <u>fame</u> from his poetry until after his death. Keats's talent was not recognized because he did not have the advantages of social position, wealth, or education. In fact, Keats grew up and lived in poverty and hardship for most of his life. However, Keats did not allow these problems to destroy his <u>passion</u> for poetry. He engaged in this lifelong <u>pursuit</u> in the face of these difficulties.

Both of Keats's parents were dead by the time he was ten years old, and he and his siblings were faced with a life of poverty. Pursuing a literary life was outside the <u>realms</u> of possibility for young Keats, and he decided to train to become a surgeon. This decision did not cause his love for literature to <u>dissolve</u>; he read widely while he was in school, and he wrote his first poem, "Lines in Imitation of Spenser," in 1814, while he was training in surgery in London.

Keats published his first book of poems in 1817. At around this time, he was forced to care for his brother, Tom, who was very ill with tuberculosis. Eventually, Keats's brother died, and Keats was greatly saddened by this loss.

Keats published his second volume of poetry in 1820, and he received great acclaim for it. However, he soon discovered that he was not <u>immortal</u>; he was ill with the same disease that killed his brother, Tom.

Keats moved to Italy, where he hoped that the milder climate would improve his health. He died in 1821, at the age of twenty-five. His poetry, filled to the <u>brim</u> with beautiful images, is still enjoyed by many people. These poetic images and the <u>rhyme</u> in which he conveys them gave him the renown he never had while he was alive.

1. Underline the phrase that tells when Keats gained <u>fame</u> from his poetry. What is a synonym for *fame*?

2. Underline the sentence that supports the idea that poverty and hardship did not destroy Keats's <u>passion</u> for poetry. Tell what *passion* means.

3. Underline the phrase that tells how Keats engaged in his life-long <u>pursuit</u> of writing poetry. Tell what *pursuit* means.

4. Underline the phrase that tells what Keats decided to pursue, since having a literary career was outside of the <u>realms</u> of possibility for him. Tell what *realms* means.

5. Underline the phrase that supports the idea that Keats's decision to train as a surgeon did not cause his love for literature to <u>dissolve</u>. What is a synonym for *dissolve*?

6. Underline the phrase that tells how Keats knew that he was not <u>immortal</u>. Tell what *immortal* means.

7. With what was Keats's poetry filled to the <u>brim</u>? Tell what *brim* means.

8. Underline the phrase that tells what the images and the <u>rhyme</u> in which Keats conveys them gave Keats. Tell what *rhyme* means.

Selected Poetry of John Keats
Reading Warm-up B

Read the following passage. Pay special attention to the underlined words. Then, read it again, and complete the activities. Use a separate sheet of paper for your written answers.

Readers of Romantic poetry <u>relish</u> the images and rich language found in John Keats's work. It is filled with images that are carefully and gracefully described by the poet. Keats was known for his love of the country, and this <u>attitude</u> is found throughout his poetry.

Keats believed that the deepest meaning of life was found in the understanding of the <u>lustrous</u> beauty surrounding him. He expressed this idea within his poetry. Some of his most famous poems, including "Ode to a Nightingale" and "Ode on a Grecian Urn," praise the beauty found in nature and created by man.

According to his friend, Charles Brown, Keats wrote "Ode to a Nightingale" in response to the joy he felt in hearing the bird's song. This song eased the <u>forlorn</u> feelings Keats may have experienced at that time due to his failing health, his sadness over his brother's death, and his inability to marry his beloved. In the poem, Keats describes the temporary pleasure he gets from listening to the bird's song, in the face of the pain that he suffers.

In "Ode on a Grecian Urn," Keats described the images from Greek <u>legend</u> that were painted upon an ancient vase. In this poem, he notes that the beauty of the urn will never <u>cease</u>, as it is permanently captured within its art. As Keats concludes in this poem "'Beauty is truth, truth beauty'—that is all/Ye know on earth, and all ye need to know."

Unfortunately, we will never know the extent to which Keats would have developed as a poet. His life was cut short by the <u>perilous</u> effects of tuberculosis. He attempted to overcome this illness by moving <u>abroad</u> to Italy in order to live in a warmer climate, but he was unsuccessful. Keats died in Italy at the age of twenty-five.

1. Underline the phrase that tells what readers of Romantic poetry <u>relish</u> about Keats's work. What is a synonym for *relish*?

2. Circle the word that describes Keats's <u>attitude</u> about the country. Tell what *attitude* means.

3. Underline the phrase that explains why the <u>lustrous</u> beauty surrounding Keats was important to him. Tell what *lustrous* means.

4. Underline the phrase that explains why might Keats have experienced <u>forlorn</u> feelings at the time he wrote "Ode to a Nightingale." Tell what *forlorn* means.

5. Underline the phrase that tells how Keats used images from Greek <u>legend</u> to convey his message in "Ode on a Grecian Urn." Use *legend* in a sentence.

6. Why won't the beauty of the urn <u>cease</u>? What is an antonym for *cease*?

7. Underline the sentence that explains how Keats attempted to overcome the <u>perilous</u> effects of tuberculosis. Use *perilous* in a sentence.

8. Circle the word that tells to where Keats moved <u>abroad</u>. Tell what *abroad* means.

Poetry of John Keats
Literary Analysis: Ode

The **ode** is a long lyric poem with a serious subject. Written in an elevated style, the ode usually honors its subject and addresses it directly. There are three types of odes in English. The **Pindaric ode** is written in sets of three stanzas and is modeled after the odes of the Greek poet Pindar. Pindar's odes were chanted by a chorus onstage, in the Greek dramatic tradition. With the first stanza, or strophe, the chorus moved to the right; with the second, or antistrophe, it moved to the left. For the third and final stanza, or epode, the chorus stood still. In the English Pindaric ode, the strophes and antistrophes have one stanza pattern and the epode has another. The **Horatian ode** is modeled after the odes of the Roman poet Horace. It is homostrophic, or contains only one type of stanza, and tends to be more restrained and meditative in tone. Finally, the **irregular ode** contains no set strophic pattern.

DIRECTIONS: *Fill in the following table to determine which type of odes Keats has written. When analyzing the stanzas, be sure to count out the number of lines, rhyme scheme, and meter for each stanza.*

	"Ode to a Nightingale"	"Ode on a Grecian Urn"
Number of stanzas		
Number of lines per stanza		
Rhyme scheme(s)		
Meter(s)		
Type of ode		

Poetry of John Keats
Reading Strategy: Paraphrase

Keats's nineteenth-century language and complex figures of speech can be difficult to understand. If you come to the end of a stanza and have no idea what you have just read, go back and read each phrase or sentence one at a time. Once you've identified the spots that are giving you trouble, you can **paraphrase** them, or restate them in your own words. Read the following example from Keats's "On First Looking into Chapman's Homer":

> Oft of one wide expanse had I been told
> That deep-browed Homer ruled as his demesne:
> Yet did I never breathe its pure serene
> Till I heard Chapman speak out loud and bold. . . .

Paraphrase:

> I had often been told of a great place, ruled by the thoughtful Homer. However, I never breathed its pure air until I heard Chapman speak of it loudly and boldly.

The paraphrased version uses simple words and phrases in the place of more difficult ones and rearranges the order of the sentence parts. Once you have paraphrased the passage you can more easily see that the "wide expanse," or "great place," refers to Homer's poetry and that Chapman's speaking of this place refers to his translation of Homer's work.

DIRECTIONS: *Paraphrase the following difficult passages from Keats's poems. Use the footnotes and a dictionary, if necessary, to define difficult words.*

from "When I Have Fears That I May Cease to Be":

1. "When I have fears that I may cease to be
   Before my pen has gleaned my teeming brain . . ."

   _____

   _____

from "Ode to a Nightingale":

2. "Fade far away, dissolve, and quite forget
   What thou among the leaves hast never known,
   The weariness, the fever, and the fret. . . ."

   _____

   _____

   _____

Name _____ Date _____

Poetry of John Keats
Vocabulary Builder

Using the Suffix -age

A. DIRECTIONS: *Each of the following sentences contains an italicized word ending with the suffix -age, one meaning of which is "state, condition, or quality." Using the word's context along with what you know about this suffix, write a definition of each italicized word in the blank.*

1. The backyard always floods because of poor *drainage.*

   _____

2. Alfred and Olivia wanted nothing more than to be joined in *marriage.*

   _____

3. The terrorists kept their prisoners in *bondage* for thirty days.

   _____

4. The war led to a great *shortage* of many goods.

   _____

5. The garage and its contents lay in *wreckage* around me.

   _____

Using the Word List

ken	surmise	gleaned
teeming	vintage	requiem

B. DIRECTIONS: *Fill in the blank in each sentence with the correct word from the Word List.*

1. I _____ that the trouble began long before we got here.
2. He _____ as much information as he could from the newspaper article.
3. The cathedral choir sang a _____ at his funeral.
4. Jack just bought a Model T to add to his collection of _____ cars.
5. The bag of rotten apples was _____ with ants.
6. The secrets of the universe are far beyond my _____.

Poetry of John Keats
Grammar and Style: Direct Address

Direct address is the calling of a person or thing by name. Terms of direct address are generally set off by commas. This device can create a tone of intimacy and provide information about the person or thing being addressed as well as the writer's thoughts or feelings about the subject being addressed. The following lines from "When I Have Fears That I May Cease to Be" show the use of direct address:

> And when I feel, *fair creature of an hour,*
> That I shall never look upon thee more . . .

A. PRACTICE: *The following passages from "Ode on a Grecian Urn" contain examples of direct address. Underline the words of direct address within each passage.*

1. Thou still unravished bride of quietness
   Thou foster child of silence and slow time,
   Sylvan historian, who canst thus express
   A flowery tale more sweetly than our rhyme . . .

2. Fair youth, beneath the trees, thou canst not leave
   Thy song, nor ever can those trees be bare. . . .

3. Ah, happy, happy boughs! that cannot shed
   Your leaves, nor ever bid the Spring adieu . . .

4. O Attic shape! Fair attitude! with brede
   Of marble men and maidens overwrought . . .

B. Writing Application: *Rewrite the following sentences using one form of direct address in each sentence.*

1. I wish I could forget you and your wicked birds.

   _____

2. Some day you will all see that I'm no child, that I knew the truth.

   _____

3. If only you would look my way, you'd know my mind.

   _____

4. I wonder what secrets hide behind those bricks of yours.

   _____

5. Did you know that the sight of you knocks me speechless?

   _____

Name _____ Date _____

Support for Writing

Complete the chart below by writing quotations about extreme feelings or ideas from two of Keats's poems. Then, think about the quotations and draw a conclusion.

Quotations Expressing Feelings and Ideas

	Poem title: _____ _____	Poem title: _____ _____
Expresses extreme feelings	Quotation:	Quotation:
	Quotation:	Quotation:
Expresses balanced feelings	Quotation:	Quotation:
	Quotation:	Quotation:

Conclusion: _____

_____

_____

_____

On a separate page, draw on information from the chart to support your response to literature.

Name _____ Date _____

Poetry of John Keats
Support for Extend Your Learning

Listening and Speaking

Use these questions to collect and organize ideas for an **oral report.**

What are the Elgin Marbles? _____

_____

_____

How did they get to England? _____

_____

_____

How did Keats learn about them? _____

_____

_____

How did the marbles influence Keats? _____

_____

_____

Research and Technology

Use this chart to record information for your **science display.** Add one or more additional categories.

The Nightingale

Categories	Information
Habitat	
Appearance	
Behavior	
Other _____ _____	

Name _____ Date _____

Poetry of John Keats
Enrichment: Greek Art

The Romantic poets shared an interest in the art, literature, and philosophy of classical antiquity. In "Ode on a Grecian Urn," Keats describes in great detail the figures painted on an urn from ancient Greece. Although he does not describe an actual urn, this description generally fits the urns, or vases, from an ancient Greek tradition of vase painting. This tradition was at its height from the late seventh century B.C. to around 475 B.C. Artists made vases out of a fine Athenian clay, which had a warm orange-red color. Then, using a glaze, they painted figures and scenes on the vase; this glaze turned black when the vase was fired. Later in this period, artists began to reverse the pictures, painting the background black while leaving the figures unglazed and red. Figures depicted on these vases include many characters from Greek mythology as well as historical figures. Vase painters frequently signed their works and received as much acclaim and prestige as other artists.

A. DIRECTIONS: *Look in an encyclopedia or a book about ancient Greek art for photographs of ancient Greek vase-painting of this period and style. Choose one photograph and answer the following questions about it.*

1. What figures or scenes are depicted on your vase? Describe what you see, including the characters and the activities.

   _____

   _____

2. Based on the library or Internet information you find, what is the historical or mythological significance of these figures? Draw some conclusion about the nature of the scenes or activities and their importance in ancient Greek culture.

   _____

   _____

B. DIRECTIONS: *Try your hand at drawing a design for a vase in the style of the ancient Greeks, depicting scenes from life today. When you have finished, be prepared to explain the details of your design as well as the spirit of the scene and the significance of the figures.*

Name _____ Date _____

Poetry of John Keats
Selection Test A

Critical Reading *Identify the letter of the choice that best answers the question.*

____ 1. In the first line of "On First Looking into Chapman's Homer," the speaker says, "Much have I traveled in the realms of gold." What are the "realms of gold"?
   A. classic literature of ancient Greece
   B. homes of wealthy English nobles
   C. history of previous civilizations
   D. lands of the old world

____ 2. To what does Keats compare Homer in "On First Looking into Chapman's Homer"?
   A. a poet
   B. a student
   C. a ruler
   D. a writer

____ 3. What form of poetry is "When I Have Fears"?
   A. Pindaric ode
   B. Horatian ode
   C. irregular ode
   D. sonnet

____ 4. Which is the best paraphrase of this line from "When I Have Fears"?
   When I have fears that I may cease to be
   Before my pen has gleaned my teeming brain,
   A. I am afraid that I will die before I have been able to write everything I want.
   B. I am afraid that I will die before I have learned to be a skilled writer.
   C. I am afraid that my brain has too many ideas to ever put down on paper.
   D. I am afraid that I do not have the skill to create great art.

____ 5. Which statement is the best paraphrase of these lines from "Ode to a Nightingale"?
   . . . forget
   What thou among the leaves hast never known,
   The weariness, the fever, and the fret
   Here, where men sit and hear each other groan;
   A. Forget all your weariness, fevers, and worries and listen to the groans of people.
   B. Forget the weariness, fevers, and worries of humans that you have never known.
   C. Do not let your weariness, fevers, and worries overpower your joys.
   D. Relax among the trees and hear how people complain about their lives.

Name _____ Date _____

___ 6. What is the form of Keats's poem "Ode to a Nightingale"?
A. Pindaric ode
B. Horatian ode
C. irregular ode
D. sonnet

___ 7. Which word best describes the speaker's attitude toward death in "Ode to a Nightingale"?
A. anxiety
B. horror
C. relief
D. fear

___ 8. Which statement is the best paraphrase of these lines from "Ode on a Grecian Urn"?

And, little town, thy streets forevermore
Will silent be; and not a soul to tell
Why thou art desolate, can e'er return.

A. The people from the town have lost their souls, leaving the people anxious.
B. The streets are empty and silent today, and no one is there to notice.
C. The streets of the town have been deserted by the townspeople.
D. The town will always be empty and no one will ever return to explain why.

Vocabulary and Grammar

___ 9. Which vocabulary word best completes this sentence?

Your _____ about the interpretation of "Ode on a Nightingale" may be correct.

A. ken
B. surmise
C. vintage
D. requiem

___ 10. Which sentence *incorrectly* uses a vocabulary word?
A. Keats *gleaned* many ideas from the nightingale by listening to its song.
B. His head was *teeming* with ideas, and he wanted to write them down.
C. What *requiem* was played on the poet's death?
D. The only *vintage* anyone noticed was the beautiful urn on the table.

____ **11.** Which line from Keats's poems contains a term of direct address?

  A. "Forlorn! the word is like a bell / To toll me back from thee to my sole self!"

  B. "Fair youth, beneath the trees, thou canst not leave / Thy song. . . ."

  C. "More happy love! more happy, happy love!"

  D. "Beauty is truth, truth beauty. . . ."

Essay

12. In an essay, explain the meaning of "Ode on a Grecian Urn." First, identify and explain the main idea of the poem. Then, identify at least three images from the poem, and explain how they support the main idea.

13. In an essay, compare "Ode to a Nightingale" to "Ode on a Grecian Urn." In your essay, answer these questions: What are the subjects of the two odes? How are the subjects alike? How does the speaker respond to these two subjects? Give examples from the poems to support your answers.

Poetry of John Keats
Selection Test B

Critical Reading *Identify the letter of the choice that best completes the statement or answers the question.*

____ 1. In "On First Looking Into Chapman's Homer," what does Keats mean by "the realms of gold"?
A. tropical oceans
B. foreign countries
C. literary classics
D. ancient civilizations

____ 2. In "On First Looking Into Chapman's Homer," Keats likens Homer to a
A. conqueror.
B. scientist.
C. discoverer.
D. monarch.

____ 3. Which is the best paraphrase of this excerpt from "On First Looking Into Chapman's Homer"?
. . . all his men / Looked at each other with a wild surmise—/ Silent . . .

A. All his men looked at one another in silent surprise.
B. All his men looked at one another, guessing wildly and struck silent.
C. All his men looked at one another wildly, trying to guess why they were so silent.
D. All his men looked at one another silently, quietly, and wildly.

____ 4. What do you think Keats means in these lines from "When I Have Fears That I May Cease to Be"?
I may never live to trace / Their shadows, with the magic hand of chance . . .

A. I may never live to paint pictures of them.
B. I may never have a chance to look at them again.
C. I may never leave the shadows as long as I live.
D. I may never live to write about them.

____ 5. For the speaker of "Ode to a Nightingale," the nightingale itself symbolizes all that is
A. rational.
B. painful.
C. timeless.
D. changeable.

____ 6. For the speaker in "Ode to a Nightingale," the idea of death is full of
A. excitement and intrigue.
B. horror and dread.
C. pleasure and delight.
D. relief and ease.

____ 7. Which describes the stanza structure of "Ode to a Nightingale"?
   A. homostrophic
   B. antistrophic
   C. strophe, antistrophe, epode
   D. no structure

____ 8. How is a Pindaric ode structured?
   A. strophe, strophe, antistrophe
   B. strophe, homostrophe, antistrophe
   C. strophe, antistrophe, epode
   D. homostrophic

____ 9. Which kind of ode is "Ode on a Grecian Urn"?
   A. Pindaric
   B. Horatian
   C. irregular
   D. devotional

____ 10. Which line best paraphrases the excerpt from "Ode to a Nightingale"?
   Away! away! for I will fly to thee,
   Not charioted by Bacchus and his pards,
   But on the viewless wings of Poesy . . .

   A. I will not visit you in your chariot but will read poems to you.
   B. I will fly to you, not on Bacchus's wings but with my own wings.
   C. I will fly to you, not drunk with wine but on the wings of fantasy.
   D. I will fly with you and Bacchus, reading poems.

____ 11. Which line best paraphrases the excerpt from "Ode on a Grecian Urn"?
   Ah, happy, happy boughs! that cannot shed
   Your leaves, nor ever bid the Spring adieu . . .

   A. Happy branches, that will never see the spring again . . .
   B. Happy branches, you will never weep at the end of spring . . .
   C. Happy branches, that will never lose your leaves or speak a single word . . .
   D. Happy branches, that will never lose your leaves or leave the springtime . . .

____ 12. For Keats in "Ode on a Grecian Urn," the lovers pictured on the urn symbolize his
   A. eternal youth and hope.
   B. maturation and full fruition.
   C. despair and frustrated desire.
   D. deep satisfaction and fulfillment.

Vocabulary and Grammar

____ 13. What does the word *ken* mean?
   A. large body of water
   B. range of sight or knowledge
   C. galaxy
   D. way of thinking

____ 14. Which word means the opposite of *teeming*?
   A. tired
   B. stupid
   C. empty
   D. old

____ 15. The word *gleaned* means
   A. examined.
   B. picked or gathered.
   C. worn out.
   D. emptied.

____ 16. Which line from "Ode to a Nightingale" contains an example of direct address?
   A. "O, for a draft of vintage!"
   B. "Thou wast not born for death, immortal Bird!"
   C. "Forlorn! The very word is like a bell . . ."
   D. "Was it a vision, or a waking dream?"

____ 17. Which quotation from "Ode on a Grecian Urn" contains an example of direct address?
   A. "Heard melodies are sweet, but those unheard / Are sweeter . . ."
   B. "Who are these coming to the sacrifice?"
   C. "What little town by river or seashore . . ."
   D. "And, little town, thy streets forevermore / Will silent be . . ."

Essay

18. In "Ode to a Nightingale" and "Ode on a Grecian Urn," Keats addresses different objects. Write an essay comparing and contrasting the objects of these two poems. Include details from the text to support your interpretation. What does he admire in the different subjects?

19. Keats deals with the concepts of mortality and immortality throughout the four poems. Write an essay about the significance of mortality and/or immortality in each of the poems, using examples from the texts. Judging by these poems and what you know about his life, why do you think he might have considered these ideas important?

Vocabulary Warm-up Word Lists

Study these words from the selection. Then, complete the activities that follow.

Word List A

bankruptcy [BANK rupt see] *n.* financial ruin
  The company declared <u>bankruptcy</u> and then went out of business.

deference [DEF uhr ens] *n.* submission; courteous respect
  In <u>deference</u> to the queen, all the people bowed when she entered the cathedral.

fraud [FRAWD] *n.* scheme to profit by cheating someone
  Copying another company's trademark is <u>fraud</u>.

ferocity [fehr AH sit ee] *n.* state of being fierce
  Lions hunt with <u>ferocity</u>, especially when they are hungry.

fluctuating [FLUK shoo ay ting] *v.* rising and falling
  The price of imports has been <u>fluctuating</u> as the dollar goes up and down in value.

impediments [im PED uh muhnts] *n.* barriers; difficulties
  Arriving late and cutting class are <u>impediments</u> to learning.

reformed [ree FOHRMD] *v.* changed for the better
  Lawmakers <u>reformed</u> the old law so that it would benefit more people.

speculate [SPEK yoo layt] *v.* weigh different ideas; guess
  I often <u>speculate</u> about my future and what life after high school will be like.

Word List B

accomplices [uh KAHM plis uhz] *n.* associates in wrongdoing
  Because the robbery was so complex, there were many <u>accomplices</u>.

emancipate [ee MAN si payt] *v.* liberate from oppression
  Abraham Lincoln signed a proclamation to <u>emancipate</u> the slaves.

exalted [eg ZAWL tuhd] *adj.* lifted up; heightened
  <u>Exalted</u> and beloved, the leader received a standing ovation.

famished [FAM isht] *adj.* extremely hungry
  Because floods washed away much of their food, the animals were <u>famished</u>.

felony [FEL uh nee] *v.* serious crime
  Theft can be a <u>felony</u>.

majority [muh JOHR uh tee] *n.* more than half of a group
  The <u>majority</u> of students voted for Dan as class president.

prescriptions [pri SKRIP shuhnz] *n.* suggested or authorized treatments
  Both girls need <u>prescriptions</u> for allergy medicine.

terminate [TER min ayt] *v.* end
  The festivities will <u>terminate</u> in a grand display of fireworks.

Name _____ Date _____

Political Commentary by George Gordon, Lord Byron, Percy Bysshe Shelley, and Thomas Babington Macaulay

Vocabulary Warm-up Exercises

Exercise A *Fill in each blank below using the appropriate word from Word List A.*

It was a sad day when the town's oldest business finally declared [1] _____,
having run out of funds. The company had been [2] _____ between survival
and financial ruin for months. In fact, people began to [3] _____ about how
a successful company could have financial problems. There were even rumors of
[4] _____ and other kinds of unfair practices by the management. The
rumors proved true. No one had detected this deception earlier because the company's
finances were difficult to sort through, creating many [5] _____ to any
investigation. The company had also been protected by people's respect, in
[6] _____ to its long history in the town. After the company's closing, many
workers protested with great [7] _____, angry that their livelihoods had dis-
appeared. Within a year, some former employees restarted the company with
[8] _____ business practices that they hoped would restore its old
reputation.

Exercise B *Decide whether each statement is true or false. Circle T or F, and explain your answer.*

1. A <u>felony</u> is a good deed.
   T / F _____

2. The commander-in-chief of a military force has an <u>exalted</u> position in combat.
   T / F _____

3. A dead-end street does not <u>terminate</u>, but it keeps on going as far as the eye can see.
   T / F _____

4. You need to have <u>prescriptions</u> filled in order to receive certain medications.
   T / F _____

5. If you are <u>famished</u>, you do not want to eat another bite of food.
   T / F _____

6. A <u>majority</u> of the people in the United States own a telephone.
   T / F _____

7. The Civil War was fought to <u>emancipate</u> the slaves.
   T / F _____

8. <u>Accomplices</u> assist others in performing charity work.
   T / F _____

Political Commentary by George Gordon, Lord Byron, Percy Bysshe Shelley, and Thomas Babington Macaulay

Reading Warm-up A

Read the following passage. Pay special attention to the underlined words. Then, read it again, and complete the activities. Use a separate sheet of paper for your written answers.

The term "Industrial Revolution" describes a process that underlined reformed and speeded up the way people produced goods, making manufacturing more efficient. This movement began in Great Britain in the late-eighteenth century, when steam was used to power machinery in factories. Industrialization seized England with a kind of ferocity in the nineteenth century, changing the world forever.

Many historians believe that the Industrial Revolution began in England because that nation had fewer impediments to new technology—not much stood in the way of advancement. England was prosperous and could spend money on new inventions. Businesses on the verge of bankruptcy struggled to stay afloat from day to day; prosperous businesses could afford to look to the future. Unlike their British counterparts, many European businesses of the period were victims of fraud and theft, and so could not invest in industrialization for a while.

Historians speculate about other reasons for the Industrial Revolution's success in Great Britain. Some think the belief of the British people in progress and technology was a major cause. There was a deference among many British people to the value of hard work, almost to the point of reverence, and a faith that the new methods and products would be successful.

The Industrial Revolution led to the development of the factory. People moved from the countryside to industrial centers. Because factories required a labor force that was stable in size, not fluctuating, housing was often provided to keep workers living nearby. Villagers became factory workers, flocking to cities, which grew tremendously.

By the late-nineteenth century, the Industrial Revolution had spread throughout Europe and the United States. Indeed, one could argue that it is still going on, as countries in Asia and South America are still moving toward an industrial way of life.

1. Underline the words that tell what the Industrial Revolution **reformed**. Tell what **reformed** means.

2. Underline the phrase that tells when the Industrial Revolution seized England with **ferocity**. What is another word that means about the same as **ferocity**?

3. Circle the words that explain what **impediments** means. What is an antonym to **impediments**?

4. Underline the phrase that tells what the businesses that were not on the verge of **bankruptcy** could do. Use **bankruptcy** in a sentence.

5. Circle the word that gives a clue about the meaning of **fraud**. What might happen to a person who commits **fraud**?

6. Circle the word in the next sentence that gives a clue to what **speculate** means. Use **speculate** in a sentence.

7. Underline the word that gives a clue to the meaning of **deference**. Give an example of a person who typically receives **deference** from others.

8. Circle the word that means the opposite of **fluctuating**. Use **fluctuating** in a sentence.

Political Commentary by George Gordon, Lord Byron, Percy Bysshe Shelley,
and Thomas Babington Macaulay
Reading Warm-up B

Read the following passage. Pay special attention to the underlined words. Then, read it again, and complete the activities. Use a separate sheet of paper for your written answers.

Lord Byron's speech to the British Parliament opposed using the death penalty to punish those who joined in the Luddite riots. These riots had broken out when unemployed weavers destroyed factory equipment that they felt threatened their ability to work.

Byron's speech, with its bitter scorn and high-flying, underline exalted language, powerfully condemns the government. He says that Parliament has adopted policies that hurt the country's poor. In fact, Byron almost accuses the government's leaders of being accomplices in the rioters' crimes. Because the leaders did nothing to help these workers, they therefore have no right to put them to death.

When Byron discusses the crimes of the poor people, he explains how each felony was actually a gesture of desperation. He says that the country's long war against Napoleon worsened economic conditions for all. Many Britons, and not simply the lower classes, had engaged in criminal actions. Men trying to feed their famished families resorted to theft and worse crimes. He says that people whose lives had been made so wretched should not be punished for their desperate attempts to survive.

Byron's speech expresses great anger at the House of Lords for seeking to punish poor people rather than emancipate them from their misery. During Byron's time, the vast majority of people in England had little income. Only a relatively small part of the population were financially comfortable. Byron feels that the government's prescriptions would do nothing to cure the ills of the poor. These measures would not terminate their suffering, but rather prolong and even worsen it. Byron's passionate attack on members of his own class in defense of the poor is powerful even today.

1. Underline the words that give a clue about the meaning of exalted. Give an example of something that is often *exalted*.

2. Underline the words that identify the accomplices Byron describes. Tell what *accomplices* means.

3. Circle the word that is close in meaning to felony. Use *felony* in a sentence.

4. Underline the word that gives a clue to the meaning of famished. What is a synonym for *famished*?

5. Circle the word that tells from what the House of Lords could emancipate the poor. Use *emancipate* in a sentence.

6. Underline the words that suggest the opposite of majority. What does it mean when an organization requires a *majority* vote to pass new rules?

7. Circle the words that identify who would not be helped by the prescriptions of England's leaders. Tell what *prescriptions* means.

8. Circle the word that is the opposite of terminate. How might a charity group work to *terminate* people's suffering?

"Speech to Parliament: In Defense of the Lower Classes" by George Gordon, Lord Byron
"A Song: 'Men of England'" by Percy Bysshe Shelley
"On the Passing of the Reform Bill" by Thomas Babington Macaulay
Literary Analysis: Political Commentary

    Political commentary, or opinions on political and social issues, can be delivered in a variety of literary forms, including speeches, essays, poems, letters, and even novels. Effective political commentators identify the ideas they wish to express, choose an appropriate literary form, and tailor their message to a particular audience. For instance, the subject of Lord Byron's commentary is a defense of the actions of workers who destroyed factory equipment to protest losing their jobs. Knowing that his audience would be members of Parliament, Byron wrote his commentary as a speech and addressed his remarks (in respectful but confrontational language) directly to his listeners. Being a member of the House of Lords as well as a poet, Byron understood that oration was the most productive form for communicating ideas to a large group of statesmen. He also believed that his fellow legislators must be challenged openly about their responsibilities toward the unemployed workers.

DIRECTIONS: *Choose one of the three literary works in this section. After reading the selection, answer the following questions.*

1. How would you describe the author's message in a sentence or two? Identify two or three sentences in which the author addresses this central idea.

   _____

   _____

   _____

2. What goal do you think the author hopes to achieve with this commentary?

   _____

   _____

   _____

3. Why do you think the author chose to write in this literary form?

   _____

   _____

   _____

4. How would you describe the audience for this political commentary?

   _____

   _____

   _____

5. List several examples of language or ideas that reflect the author's awareness of his audience.

   _____

   _____

   _____

"Speech to Parliament: In Defense of the Lower Classes" by George Gordon, Lord Byron
"A Song: 'Men of England'" by Percy Bysshe Shelley
"On the Passing of the Reform Bill" by Thomas Babington Macaulay
Reading Strategy: Set a Purpose for Reading

If you **set a purpose for reading,** you can focus your attention on particular aspects of a literary work and enrich your reading experience. For instance, if you decide to read "A Song: 'Men of England'" for pleasure, you might take special note of Shelley's use of language, his sound devices, and his passionate tone. On the other hand, you could choose to read the poem to identify its Romantic characteristics; in this case, you might pay close attention to the poet's use of nature imagery and to his challenging attitude about employers' poor treatment of workers.

DIRECTIONS: *This graphic organizer can help you set a purpose for reading, note specific passages in the literature, and reflect on these passages in light of your purpose. Before reading, state your purpose in the center box. Then, as you read, write down at least four passages from the work that relate to or answer your purpose. Beneath each quoted passage, explain how it deepens your understanding and helps fulfill your purpose.*

Purpose

Passages

"Speech to Parliament: In Defense of the Lower Classes" by George Gordon, Lord Byron
"A Song: 'Men of England'" by Percy Bysshe Shelley
"On the Passing of the Reform Bill" by Thomas Babington Macaulay

Vocabulary Builder

Using the Roots -*dec*-

A. DIRECTIONS: *Each of the words in the left column contains the roots -deci- or -deca-, meaning "ten." Match each word with its definition in the right column. Write the letter of the definition on the line next to the word it defines.*

___ 1. decade

___ 2. decimal

___ 3. decahedron

___ 4. decibel

___ 5. decathlon

A. an athletic contest consisting of ten events

B. a solid figure with ten plane surfaces

C. a period of ten years

D. a fraction expressed in base 10

E. a numerical expression of the relative loudness of sounds

Using the Word List

impediments	decimation	efficacious
emancipate	balm	inauspicious

B. DIRECTIONS: *Choose the letter of the word or phrase that is most nearly the same as each numbered word. Write the letters on the lines provided.*

___ 1. inauspicious
  A. unlikeable
  B. unmentionable
  C. unfavorable
  D. uneasy

___ 2. emancipate
  A. trap
  B. free
  C. enliven
  D. elevate

___ 3. balm
  A. something disturbing
  B. something healing
  C. something flat
  D. something powdery

___ 4. efficacious
  A. affluent
  B. effusive
  C. efficient
  D. effective

___ 5. impediments
  A. obstructions
  B. detours
  C. pedestals
  D. openings

___ 6. decimation
  A. harm
  B. destruction
  C. support
  D. addition

"Speech to Parliament: In Defense of the Lower Classes" by George Gordon, Lord Byron
"A Song: 'Men of England'" by Percy Bysshe Shelley
"On the Passing of the Reform Bill" by Thomas Babington Macaulay
Grammar and Style: Correlative Conjunctions

Correlative conjunctions work in pairs to link two words or groups of words of equal importance. Writers use correlative conjunctions such as *just as . . . so (too)* and *whether . . . or,* to present their ideas in a balanced manner. The following lines from "Speech to Parliament: In Defense of the Lower Classes" show how a pair of correlative conjunctions works in a sentence.

> When we were told that these men are leagued together, *not only* for the destruction of their own comfort, *but* of their very means of subsistence, can we forget that it is the bitter policy . . . unto the third and fourth generation!

A. PRACTICE: *Underline the correlative conjunctions in each of the following sentences.*

1. It is widely believed that both Shelley and Byron are among the most important English poets of the early nineteenth century.

2. Do you know whether Lord Byron is considered a Romantic or a Victorian writer?

3. Neither Byron nor Shelley possessed Thomas Babington Macaulay's qualifications as a statesman.

4. Just as repetition can underscore a poem's musicality, so too can it intensify the persuasiveness of a piece of oration.

5. The anthology contains not only examples of Shelley's verses but also a selection of his personal letters.

B. Writing Application: *Rewrite each pair of sentences below as a single sentence. In your sentence, use the pair of correlative conjunctions that appears in brackets.*

1. You may write your research report on the life and literary works of Percy Bysshe Shelley. You may write your report on the life and literary works of Mary Shelley. [*either . . . or*]

_____

2. Poets must consider carefully the connotations of the words they choose to express their ideas. Poets must consider with great care the sound of the words they use. [*not only . . . but also*]

_____

3. If you are writing a speech, you must pay close attention to your audience. If you are writing a persuasive essay, you must pay close attention to your audience. [*whether . . . or*]

_____

Name _____ Date _____

"Speech to Parliament: In Defense of the Lower Classes" by George Gordon, Lord Byron
"A Song: 'Men of England'" by Percy Bysshe Shelley
"On the Passing of the Reform Bill" by Thomas Babington Macaulay
Support for Writing

Use the chart below to take notes for your editorial. First, write down the issue you want to argue in the first line. Then, gather and jot down the facts about the issue. After you have had a chance to gather and think about the facts, state your opinion.

Political issue:	
Who?	
What?	
When?	
Where?	
Why?	
How	
My opinion:	

On a separate page, use information from the chart to help you write your editorial. You will probably want to revise how you stated your opinion in the chart as you work it into your editorial. Use details from the chart to support your position.

"Speech to Parliament: In Defense of the Lower Classes" by George Gordon, Lord Byron
"A Song: 'Men of England'" by Percy Bysshe Shelley
"On the Passing of the Reform Bill" by Thomas Babington Macaulay
Support for Extend Your Learning

Listening and Speaking

Use the following checklist as you practice reading Byron's **speech.** After your first reading, rate your performance on a scale of 1–10, or have a partner rate you. Then, think of ways to improve your delivery.

Checklist for Delivering a Speech

Techniques	Rating	How I can improve my techniques
Raise or lower voice for stress		
Change tone		
Emphasize rhetorical questions		
Slow down or speed up rate of reading		
Hand gestures and facial expressions		

Research and Technology

Use the chart to organize and gather information for your opinion **report.** List specific details about the source of your information.

Issue: _____

Source		Details
	page:	
	page:	
	page:	

"Speech to Parliament: In Defense of the Lower Classes" by George Gordon, Lord Byron
"A Song: 'Men of England'" by Percy Bysshe Shelley
"On the Passing of the Reform Bill" by Thomas Babington Macaulay
Enrichment: Political Commentary

Despite the dramatically different forms of their political commentaries, Shelley, Byron, and Macaulay each begin by focusing on a social problem they believed needed to be changed. Think about contemporary situations or conflicts affecting you or others in your school or community. In your opinion, what can be done to bring about better conditions? A letter, poem, speech, or other kind of composition can be an effective way to make a case for change.

DIRECTIONS: *Focus on a single local issue or problem and follow the steps below to draft a piece of political commentary. Write your responses on a separate sheet of paper.*

1. In one or two sentences, state clearly the **topic** you wish to address.

2. Who will be the **audience** for your writing? You may be able to choose this audience (as Macaulay did), or it may be determined for you (as it was for Byron) by circumstances related to the issue. List specific characteristics of your audience, such as their ages, genders, special interests, and levels of education. Is your audience knowledgeable about or emotionally involved with this topic? How will these factors influence the way you write?

3. Given your topic and audience, will your political commentary be most effective in the **form** of a letter, poem, or speech? Why?

4. What **tone** is appropriate for your topic and audience? What, if any, special language requirements will you need to consider? For instance, Byron's and Macaulay's sophisticated language is well-suited to their highly educated audiences, whereas Shelley employs simpler diction and sentence structure to reach a broader audience.

5. What **organization** will make your argument most effective? Possible organizational plans include main idea and details, order-of-importance, chronological order, cause/effect, comparison/contrast, pro and con, question and answer, and part/whole. Shelley's ideas are arranged as a series of questions and answers, whereas Macaulay uses chronological order to provide a narrative account. Lord Byron uses two strategies to organize his speech: He begins by explaining the causes of unrest among lower-class workers and the effect of Parliamentary policy on their condition; then he turns to a question and answer arrangement—in fact, to a long series of rhetorical questions followed by a rather sarcastic answer.

"Speech to Parliament" by George Gordon, Lord Byron
"A Song: 'Men of England'" by Percy Bysshe Shelley
"On the Passing of the Reform Bill" by Thomas Babington Macaulay

Selection Test A

Critical Reading *Identify the letter of the choice that best answers the question.*

____ 1. In Byron's "Speech to Parliament," he tries to convince Parliament not to severely punish the weavers for an action they have taken. What did they do?

    A. The workers went on strike.

    B. The workers destroyed their looms.

    C. The workers rioted in the streets.

    D. The workers refused to work overtime.

____ 2. According to Byron in "Speech to Parliament," what punishment is Parliament considering for the weavers' crimes?

    A. loss of jobs

    B. imprisonment

    C. death

    D. high fines

____ 3. Which of the following would be an ineffective purpose for reading "Speech to Parliament"?

    A. to learn about British class divisions

    B. to decide how Byron appeals to the hearts of his listeners

    C. to discover what kinds of persuasive devices Byron uses

    D. to analyze Byron's poetic techniques

____ 4. What argument does Byron make in his "Speech to Parliament" to persuade members of Parliament that the actions they are considering are too harsh?

    A. Serious crimes are committed by people much better off than the weavers.

    B. The weavers could have committed far more destructive crimes.

    C. The weavers have already lost their jobs, so there is no point in punishing them more.

    D. No one was hurt by the weavers' actions, so they should not be considered criminals.

___ 5. Which choice best describes this line from Percy Bysshe Shelley's "A Song: 'Men of England'"?

> Men of England, wherefore plough
> For the lords who lay ye low?

   A. balanced clauses
   B. rhetorical question
   C. evidence
   D. assumption

___ 6. Which of the following would be the least effective purpose for reading "A Song: 'Men of England'"?
   A. to analyze Shelley's use of poetic devices
   B. to learn the conditions of workers in early nineteenth-century England
   C. to study the history of production technology in the textile industry
   D. to learn more about Shelley and his attitudes and philosophy

___ 7. What attitude does Shelley express in "A Song: 'Men of England'" toward working conditions in England?
   A. bitter
   B. hopeful
   C. humorous
   D. forgiving

___ 8. What is the biggest difference between the audiences for Macaulay's "On the Passing of the Reform Bill" and Byron's "Speech to Parliament"?
   A. Macaulay's audience is known to him, whereas Byron's audience is not.
   B. Macaulay's audience is better educated than Byron's.
   C. Macaulay's audience disagrees with him, but Byron's supports his cause.
   D. Macaulay has an audience of one person, while Byron speaks to many.

Vocabulary and Grammar

___ 9. Which vocabulary word best completes this sentence?

> In spite of the _____ to passing the Reform Bill, Parliament finally approved it in 1832.

   A. impediments
   B. decimation
   C. emancipation
   D. balm

_____ **10.** Which word means the *opposite* of *efficacious*, as it is used in this sentence?

Delaying the vote was *efficacious* because it allowed members of Parliament to learn what the people in their districts thought about the bill.

A. inefficient

B. unreasonable

C. useless

D. critical

_____ **11.** Which line from "Speech to Parliament" contains correlative conjunctions?

A. "I have traversed the seat of war in the Peninsula; I have been in some of the most oppressed provinces of Turkey. . . ."

B. "These men were willing to dig, but the spade was in other hands. . . ."

C. "After feeling the pulse and shaking the head over the patient . . . these convulsions must terminate in death. . . ."

D. ". . . we are told that these men are leagued together, not only for the destruction of their own comfort, but of their very means of subsistence. . . ."

Essay

12. In "A Song: 'Men of England,'" Shelley uses numerous images of nature. In an essay, identify some of these images. How does Shelley use the images to make his point? To what does he compare them? Explain how you think the images are effective in supporting his arguments.

13. In an essay, summarize Byron's argument in "Speech Before Parliament." What are the main reasons he gives to support his viewpoint? Is his argument convincing? Give at least two examples to support your summary.

"Speech to Parliament: In Defense of the Lower Classes" by George Gordon, Lord Byron
"A Song: 'Men of England'" by Percy Bysshe Shelley
"On the Passing of the Reform Bill" by Thomas Babington Macaulay
Selection Test B

Critical Reading *Identify the letter of the choice that best completes the statement or answers the question.*

_____ 1. In "A Song: 'Men of England,'" whom does Shelley characterize as *drones*?
  A. England's unemployed citizens
  B. political protesters
  C. society's richest and most powerful people
  D. farmers, weavers, and smiths

_____ 2. What irony does Shelley suggest by asking why English workers forge "Many a weapon, chain, and scourge"?
  A. Chains, whips, and weapons should not be used against bees.
  B. Implements that the workers make are later used against them.
  C. Punishment can be meted out in various cruel ways.
  D. English tradespeople are among the most skillful in the world.

_____ 3. In "A Song: 'Men of England'" Shelley's attitude toward his subject might best be described as _____.
  A. dignified
  B. optimistic
  C. dispassionate
  D. embittered

_____ 4. Which would be the *least* appropriate purpose for reading "A Song: 'Men of England'"?
  A. to increase your knowledge about Percy Bysshe Shelley
  B. to learn facts about production methods of textiles, agricultural products, and iron in early nineteenth-century England
  C. to appreciate poetic devices
  D. to compare the situations of early nineteenth-century English workers and contemporary American workers

_____ 5. Why might Byron have devoted the early part of his speech to a direct comparison of destructive weavers and distinguished members of the House of Lords?
  A. He wished to surprise and alienate his audience.
  B. He hoped to gain the trust and sympathy of audience members with working-class origins.
  C. He hoped to stir in his audience feelings of guilt and personal responsibility for the difficulties of the unemployed weavers.
  D. He wanted to emphasize the impressive power of the House of Lords.

____ 6. Which word best describes Byron's tone in this sentence?

That most favorite state measure, so marvelously efficacious in many and recent instances, temporizing, would not be without its advantages in this.

A. indignant
B. offhand
C. comic
D. sarcastic

____ 7. Given the title "Speech to Parliament: In Defense of the Lower Classes," which of the following purposes would have been ineffective for reading Lord Byron's commentary?
A. analyzing Byron's poetic style
B. deepening understanding of British class divisions
C. determining if Byron appeals to the hearts or the heads of his audience
D. analyzing Byron's use of rhetorical devices

____ 8. By comparing his view of a Parliamentary vote to "seeing Caesar stabbed in the Senate House" and "seeing Oliver [Cromwell] taking the mace from the table," Thomas Babington Macaulay emphasizes
A. that supporting the Reform Bill is akin to committing a criminal act.
B. his own long, distinguished political career.
C. the historical significance of the passage of the Reform Bill.
D. that the Reform Bill will benefit politicians as well as ordinary citizens.

____ 9. What is the purpose of a political commentary?
A. to persuade readers to take some particular action
B. to support an original political argument with examples and explanations from literature
C. to express opinions on political issues
D. to use rhetorical devices to clarify the need for social change

____ 10. One reason for setting a purpose for reading is to
A. improve your reading rate.
B. make a piece of literature easier to summarize.
C. make literary works seem more vivid and accessible.
D. focus and deepen your experience of a piece of literature.

____ 11. What is the most important way in which Lord Byron's audience differs from that of Thomas Babington Macaulay?
A. Byron's audience is better educated than Macaulay's.
B. Byron's audience is a group of people, whereas Macaulay's is an individual.
C. Macaulay's audience knows him personally, whereas part of Byron's audience does not know him at all.
D. Unlike Macaulay's audience, Byron's is composed of experienced public speakers.

Vocabulary and Grammar

____ **12.** Which word means the opposite of *efficacious*?
   A. fruitful
   B. ineffective
   C. barren
   D. obliging

____ **13.** The word *impediments* means
   A. obstructions.
   B. tools.
   C. hourly wages.
   D. arguments.

____ **14.** Correlative conjunctions are used to
   A. introduce subordinate clauses.
   B. link grammatically equal words or groups of words.
   C. separate nonessential phrases from other words in a sentence.
   D. connect subjects and verbs.

____ **15.** Which pair of words can function as correlative conjunctions?
   A. yet, still
   B. only, also
   C. if, or
   D. neither, nor

Essay

16. In his argument against a sentence of execution for condemned British weavers, Lord Byron repeatedly uses words related to food (*famished, starving, daily bread*) and war (*destructive warfare, lancets of your military, martial law, dragooned, grenadiers*). Write an essay in which you evaluate the effectiveness of these images in Byron's political commentary. How direct is the connection between the weavers' hunger and their crimes? Is there any relationship between hunger and war? To which of the audience's emotions or human attributes do such images appeal?

17. Shelley and Byron considered themselves to be artists, yet both were also passionately political men. Using references to two or three of the selections you've just read, write an essay in which you discuss the relationship between politics and art. Is an art form such as poetry suitable for delivering political messages? Do you think politics and art are best kept separate? Is it possible to create a work of art without political content? Do the goals of the artist and the political commentator conflict with one another?

Vocabulary Warm-up Word Lists

Study these words from the selections. Then, complete the activities that follow.

Word List A

amiable [AY mee uh buhl] *adj.* friendly and agreeable
   With an amiable smile, Mr. Diaz greets his new students.

attribute [uh TRIB yoot] *v.* relate to a particular cause or source
   Dan can attribute his fine tennis game to months of practice at the club.

comprehension [kahm pree HEN shuhn] *n.* understanding
   Elizabeth has no comprehension of what happened in the story.

conscientiously [kahn shee EN shus lee] *adv.* with extreme care
   Always acting conscientiously, Amanda picks up the trash in the park.

conviction [kuhn VIK shuhn] *n.* an unshakable belief in something
   Her kind nature further fuels John's conviction of her innocence.

deficiencies [dee FISH uhn seez] *n.* shortages; insufficient amounts
   Vitamin deficiencies cause many health problems.

partial [PAR shuhl] *adj.* favoring one side over others; biased
   If the referees are partial, they are not doing their job properly.

uniformly [yoo ni FORM lee] *adv.* in a consistent manner
   Each morning, Eliza makes all the beds uniformly.

Word List B

degraded [dee GRAYD ed] *v.* reduced in grade, rank, or status
   Joel felt degraded when he was chosen last for the team.

deplore [dee PLOHR] *v.* express strong disapproval of
   I deplore the habits of poor hygiene.

equilibrium [ee kwi LIB ree uhm] *n.* a stable, balanced condition
   The Yin and Yang is a Chinese symbol of equilibrium.

fortitude [FOHR ti tood] *n.* strength of mind
   John bravely went through the difficult operation with great fortitude.

frivolous [FRIV uh luhs] *adj.* inappropriately silly
   We bought what we needed, and then made a few frivolous purchases.

gravity [GRAV i tee] *n.* seriousness or importance
   Understanding the gravity of the situation, Frank called the police.

prevalent [PREV uh luhnt] *adj.* widely or commonly occurring
   As people age, the need for eyeglasses becomes prevalent.

rational [RASH uh nuhl] *adj.* having the ability to reason
   Lucy shows rational behavior, and puts on her seatbelt in the car.

"On Making an Agreeable Marriage" by Jane Austen
from **A Vindication of the Rights of Woman** by Mary Wollstonecraft
Vocabulary Warm-up Exercises

Exercise A *Fill in the blanks, using each word from World List A only once.*

Janet has a firm [1] _____ that no one should live in poverty. She
puts her belief into practice by volunteering at the local soup kitchen, where she
[2] _____ tries to make sure that everyone gets enough to eat. She per-
forms this work with an [3] _____ smile because she believes that the people who come for help deserve friendly service. She treats everyone who comes there fairly
and [4] _____ so that they do not feel neglected. She prevents other volun-
teers from showing [5] _____ treatment toward anyone because she thinks
that showing such bias would discourage people from coming to the soup kitchen. Janet
works closely with local supermarkets to make sure that food is delivered regularly and
that there are no [6] _____ in the supply of food to the soup kitchen. Janet
gives presentations to local organizations in order to increase [7] _____
and awareness of poverty and the ways to eliminate it. She hopes that one day she will be
able to [8] _____ the end of poverty in her community to these efforts.

Exercise B *Decide whether each statement is true or false. Circle T or F, and explain your answer.*

1. If you <u>deplore</u> chocolate ice cream, you like it very much.
   T / F _____

2. Trees are <u>prevalent</u> in the Sahara Desert.
   T / F _____

3. If you have been <u>degraded</u> by someone, you have been praised by them.
   T / F _____

4. You need <u>fortitude</u> to deal with a life-threatening situation.
   T / F _____

5. Comedians tell their jokes with a sense of <u>gravity</u> in order to make people laugh.
   T / F _____

6. A <u>frivolous</u> hobby is something that you urgently need to do.
   T / F _____

7. If you have your <u>equilibrium</u>, you have your sense of balance.
   T / F _____

8. Scientists need to use <u>rational</u> thought in order to prove their theories.
   T / F _____

"On Making an Agreeable Marriage" by Jane Austen
from **A Vindication of the Rights of Woman** by Mary Wollstonecraft
Reading Warm-up A

Read the following passage. Pay special attention to the underlined words. Then, read it again, and complete the activities. Use a separate sheet of paper for your written answers.

Pat is the first woman in her family to go to college. She can <u>attribute</u> much of her success to her parents' support of her efforts. They raised her with the <u>conviction</u> that she could do anything if she put her mind to it. They are very proud of their daughter's accomplishments. Since they never had the opportunity to pursue higher education, they made sure that Pat would get the chance to undergo the challenge of a university education.

Pat made many sacrifices in order to get a college education, including studying <u>conscientiously</u> in high school, carefully reading her texts. She also read outside of class in order to increase her reading <u>comprehension</u>. As a result, Pat was able to read at the college level while she was still in high school.

Pat's dedication to studying meant that she missed many social events and activities. Although Pat was <u>partial</u> to dancing, preferring it over sports, she seldom attended the school dances because of her intense study schedule. Pat promised herself that when she reached college, she would make up for these <u>deficiencies</u> by balancing her schoolwork with her social life.

The best day of Pat's life was graduation day. She was chosen as class valedictorian, since her grades were <u>uniformly</u> and consistently the best in the class. Pat was honored by this selection, and gave her thanks in a speech that she made during the ceremony.

Pat realized that she had to make many difficult decisions in order to reach her goal. While some students were having lighthearted fun, she was expanding her intellect. Throughout this experience, Pat never forgot to be true to herself. Pat is extremely friendly and one of the most <u>amiable</u> people you would ever want to meet.

1. Underline the phrase that tells to what Pat can <u>attribute</u> much of her success. Tell what **attribute** means.

2. Underline the phrase that tells what <u>conviction</u> Pat was raised with. Tell what **conviction** means.

3. Underline the word that means about the same as <u>conscientiously</u>. What is an antonym of **conscientiously**?

4. Underline the phrase that tells what Pat did in order to increase her reading <u>comprehension</u>. Use **comprehension** in a sentence about school.

5. Circle the word that means about the same as <u>partial</u>. Describe what school activity you are **partial** to.

6. Underline the phrase that tells what <u>deficiencies</u> Pat plans to make up for. Use **deficiencies** in a sentence.

7. Circle the word that means about the same as <u>uniformly</u>. What is an antonym of **uniformly**?

8. Circle the word that tells what <u>amiable</u> means. Use **amiable** in a sentence.

"On Making an Agreeable Marriage" by Jane Austen
from **A Vindication of the Rights of Woman** by Mary Wollstonecraft
Reading Warm-up B

Read the following passage. Pay special attention to the underlined words. Then, read it again, and complete the activities. Use a separate sheet of paper for your written answers.

Mary Wollstonecraft, who lived and wrote during the eighteenth century, was a champion for women's rights. She believed that the underlined view that women were inferior to men was wrong. Mary felt that women were degraded in society, and she wanted to eliminate this debasing treatment of women.

Mary developed these beliefs while working as a schoolteacher and headmistress at a small, private school that she founded with her sisters. Her work at this school convinced her that the silly, frivolous behavior of the girls who studied there arose as a result of the way men treated them and expected them to behave. Mary came to deplore this type of silly behavior because of her observations of a mother whose children she tutored. She viewed this woman as an example of all that was wrong with the way that women were raised to behave.

As a result of these experiences, Mary worked to obtain equal educational opportunities for women. She believed that women were rational beings who were capable of the same intellectual achievements as men. Women simply needed to be provided with an equal chance in order to realize their potential. Mary's personal fortitude and passionate belief that her position was correct gave her the strength to pursue this cause.

Mary Wollstonecraft did not live to see the attainment of her goal of providing social equilibrium for women through education. She died at the age of thirty-eight, shortly after her second child was born. Nearly two centuries after her death, women in Britain would be given the right to vote. In many ways, we are indebted to her for providing a foundation and a sense of gravity for the serious cause of women's rights. Today, women have many more educational and career opportunities than they had in Mary's time.

1. Underline the phrase that tells what the underlined view of women was during Mary Wollstonecraft's time. Tell what **prevalent** means.

2. Underline the words that provide a clue to the meaning of degraded. Tell what **degraded** means.

3. Circle the word that tells what frivolous means. Use **frivolous** in a sentence.

4. Underline the phrase that tells what Mary came to deplore. If you **deplore** beans, will you eat them often? Explain your answer.

5. Underline the phrase that provides a clue to the meaning of rational. Tell what **rational** means.

6. Circle the word that is a simile for fortitude. Describe an activity that would require great **fortitude**.

7. Underline the phrase that tells when women in Britain received equilibrium in the right to vote.

8. Circle the word that provides a clue to the meaning of gravity. What is an antonym of **gravity**?

Name _____ Date _____

"On Making an Agreeable Marriage" by Jane Austen
from **A Vindication of the Rights of Woman** by Mary Wollstonecraft
Literary Analysis: Social Commentary

Mary Wollstonecraft and Jane Austen were writers who were enormously gifted in the art of **social commentary.** These women looked closely at the world around them, thought deeply about what they saw, and put their views down on paper for the betterment and enjoyment of others. For example, Austen begins her letter to her niece by gently prodding Fanny to remember all her gentleman friend's wonderful qualities. But Austen's letter slowly transforms into an appeal to consider carefully before accepting a marriage proposal, and thereby avoid a marriage of convenience or a marriage for the sake of money. Her point, in the end, is that there is nothing worse than marriage without mutual affection and respect. Austen, who remained unmarried throughout her brief life, was nonetheless able to view the institution of marriage with great perception and evenhandedness.

DIRECTIONS: *Read the excerpts from the selections and answer the questions that follow.*

> And from the time of our being in London together, I thought you really very much in love.—But you certainly are not at all—there is no concealing it.—What strange creatures we are!—It seems as if your being made secure of him (as you say yourself) had made you Indifferent.
>
> (from "On Making an Agreeable Marriage")

1. What point does Austen make about the fickle nature of some human relationships?

_____

_____

_____

_____

> It is acknowledged that they spend many of the first years of their lives in acquiring a smattering of accomplishments; meanwhile strength of body and mind are sacrificed to libertine notions of beauty, to the desire of establishing themselves—the only way women can rise in the world—by marriage. And this desire making mere animals of them, when they marry they act as such children may be expected to act—they dress, they paint, and nickname God's creatures. Can they be expected to govern a family with judgment, or take care of the poor babes whom they bring into the world?
>
> (from A Vindication of the Rights of Women)

2. What point is Wollstonecraft making about women's place in society?

_____

_____

_____

_____

_____

_____

"On Making an Agreeable Marriage" by Jane Austen
from **A Vindication of the Rights of Woman** by Mary Wollstonecraft
Reading Strategy: Determine the Writer's Purpose

It is particularly important to **determine the writer's purpose** when you're reading essays, speeches, or works of social commentary. Authors of these works can have a variety of purposes. Some seek to explain an issue or a process; others attempt to persuade a certain group or society in general to think in a particular way. Still others write to incite their audience to take action.

DIRECTIONS: *Use this graphic organizer to help you record and analyze Mary Wollstonecraft's purpose for writing "A Vindication of the Rights of Women." For each paragraph write down clues that reflect the author's tone and attitude. Decide what you think the author's purpose was. Then think about how the paragraph affected your own opinion on the topic. The first paragraph has been analyzed for you.*

Author's Tone/Attitude	Author's Purpose	Personal Reaction
Paragraph 1: The author takes a tone that reveals her to be saddened and frustrated by the way women of her generation are being educated. She feels strongly that women are sacrificing their intellects in order to gain the attentions of men. Wollstonecraft keeps her tone low-key, but it is clear that the situation she is writing about also makes her angry.	The author is attempting to persuade readers that women have been unfairly treated.	Some of the points about society that Wollstonecraft makes are still relevant today. Many women act nice or pretend they're not overly intelligent so that men won't feel threatened.
Paragraph 2:		
Paragraph 3:		
Paragraph 4:		
Paragraph 5:		

Name _____ Date _____

"On Making an Agreeable Marriage" by Jane Austen
from A Vindication of the Rights of Woman by Mary Wollstonecraft
Vocabulary Builder

Using the Root -fort-

A. DIRECTIONS: *Each of the following sentences includes an italicized word that contains the word root -fort-, meaning "strong." Fill in the blank with a word or phrase that completes the sentence and reveals the meaning of the italicized word.*

1. A musical analogy Mary Wollstonecraft might have used is that while women were expected to play the piano softly and prettily, men could be counted on to play *fortissimo*, _____.

2. The *fortress* stood upon a hill and was _____.

3. Jane Austen wrote to her friend Fanny to provide *fortification* for Fanny to make up her own mind about marriage. Austen wanted to _____ Fanny's resolve.

4. Mary Wollstonecraft put a lot of *effort* into her essay on woman's rights. It was a _____ to put her deepest feelings into words.

Using the Word List

scruple	amiable	vindication	fortitude	gravity
solicitude	fastidious	specious	preponderates	

B. DIRECTIONS: *In the following paragraph, fill in the blanks using words from the Word List.*

Jane Austen wrote to Fanny out of (1) _____ with regard to her friend's

future marriage. Austen's argument was certainly not (2) _____, or

deceptively attractive. To Austen, choosing the right husband was a matter of great

(3) _____. In Austen's mind, there was no need to provide

(4) _____ for *not* marrying someone; one either loved the other person or one

didn't. She had no regard for women who behaved in a false manner by only pretending to care

for someone. Nor did Austen advocate being so (5) _____ as to be pleased by no

man. She recommended a clear head, an open heart, and (6) _____ of spirit.

Austen's philosophy seemed to be that if one of those things (7) _____ over the

others, all is lost. Although she had no (8) _____ about speaking her mind,

Austen's tone remained (9) _____ throughout her letter to Fanny.

"On Making an Agreeable Marriage" by Jane Austen
from **A Vindication of the Rights of Woman** by Mary Wollstonecraft
Grammar and Style: Commas in a Series

It is important to be consistent when using a grammatical device such as **commas in a series.** Although it is usual to use commas in a series to ensure clear writing, modern rules of grammar also allow for omitting the final comma before a conjunction. Look at these examples.

Final comma: Jane Austen recommends that young women be amiable, discerning, and scrupulous when it comes to choosing a mate.

No final comma: She warns against loveless marriage, a fastidious nature and specious behavior.

Each of the sentences above is correct in terms of proper usage. However, if the two example sentences were to appear within the same piece of writing, they would create a consistency problem. Remember that whichever comma style you decide to employ, you must use it consistently throughout a single piece of writing.

A. PRACTICE: *Decide whether each of the sentences uses series commas appropriately. If a sentence does not use series commas correctly, rewrite the corrected sentence on the blank line. If the sentence is correct as written, write* correct *on the blank line.*

1. Fanny, and her friends, and family addressed the problem of her impending marriage.

   _____

2. You might say that honesty, happiness, and respect are the three main requirements for a happy marriage.

   _____

3. Mary Wollstonecraft felt that young women were taught to behave in a deceptive, conniving, and, ridiculous way.

   _____

B. Writing Application: *Follow the directions to create sentences that correctly use commas in a series.*

1. Write a sentence that uses three adjectives about women's societal roles according to Mary Wollstonecraft.

   _____

   _____

2. Write a sentence about the possible importance of a large family in Mary Wollstonecraft's day.

   _____

   _____

3. Write a sentence about love and marriage in Jane Austen's day.

   _____

   _____

"On Making an Agreeable Marriage" by Jane Austen
from **A Vindication of the Rights of Woman** by Mary Wollstonecraft
Support for Writing

Use the chart below to take notes for your letter to an author. Review the selection and jot down notes about the author's opinion in the first column. Then, jot down notes about your response in the second column. Include reasons and facts to support your opinion.

Author:	
Author's Opinion	**My Reaction**

On a separate page, use the information in the chart to write your letter to an author.

Name _____ Date _____

"On Making an Agreeable Marriage" by Jane Austen
from **A Vindication of the Rights of Woman** by Mary Wollstonecraft
Support for Extend Your Learning

Listening and Speaking

Review "On Making an Agreeable Marriage" and note the logical, emotional, and ethical appeals that Austen uses. Then, use the chart to record the appeals you will use in your **telephone call.**

Appeals	Appeals in Today's Language
Logical	
Emotional	
Ethical	

Research and Technology

Use the following chart to collect details for your **timeline.** Write events and the dates that occurred. When you are finished collecting information, number the events in the order that you will show them on your timeline.

Order	Date	Event in the Struggle for Women's Rights

"On Making an Agreeable Marriage" by Jane Austen
from **A Vindication of the Rights of Woman** by Mary Wollstonecraft
Enrichment: Social Studies

British Social Customs

Every writer is to some extent a product of his or her time. During the days when Jane Austen and Mary Wollstonecraft were writing, the roles of men and women were very sharply defined. Roughly speaking, men had power through their control of the family fortune, and women ran the household. The manners and customs of the time were built on the foundation of these contrasting roles. Austen and Wollstonecraft, unlike many of their female contemporaries, engaged in the "masculine" activity of refining thoughts and perceptions through writing.

Mary Wollstonecraft personified early feminism. She was not only well educated, but also extremely vocal about the rights of women. Her clear-thinking denunciation of the oppressive social mores of her day ultimately won her a place in literary history. Jane Austen's literary works are steeped in the manners of the day. Her books show all the grace—and often the idiocy—of those manners. By focusing on the place of her characters in society, Austen was able to show in great detail the elaborate social underpinnings of her time.

DIRECTIONS: *Answer the following questions about the manners and social structure of the past and the present.*

1. During a courtship in Austen and Wollstonecraft's time it was considered appropriate for a young man and a young woman to have a female chaperone—usually a friend or relative of the young woman—with them at all times. How might this custom have affected the relationship of the young couple?

_____

_____

_____

2. As Jane Austen mentions, the bulk of a man's money and land upon his death went to his eldest son. What problems do you think this might have caused for some families?

_____

_____

_____

3. As Wollstonecraft notes, young girls were encouraged to spend most of their energy on making themselves attractive and finding a husband. Is this different from the way things are today, and if so, how?

_____

_____

_____

"On Making an Agreeable Marriage" by Jane Austen
from **A Vindication of the Rights of Woman** by Mary Wollstonecraft
Selection Test A

Critical Reading *Identify the letter of the choice that best answers the question.*

_____ 1. According to Austen in "On Making an Agreeable Marriage," what is the most important reason for marrying someone?
  A. wealth
  B. personality
  C. affection
  D. respect

_____ 2. What is Jane Austen's purpose in writing to her niece Fanny in "On Making an Agreeable Marriage"?
  A. to tell her about the success of her book
  B. to advise her on marriage
  C. to share news of the family
  D. to discuss their interest in music

_____ 3. According to Austen in "On Making an Agreeable Marriage," what are Fanny's two biggest objections to her suitor?
  A. He is poor and lives far away.
  B. He is generous but lacks confidence.
  C. He is selfish and proud.
  D. He is too modest and good.

_____ 4. Why does Austen tell Fanny in "On Making an Agreeable Marriage" that "I have no hope of writing anything to the purpose"?
  A. She knows little about the man who wants to marry Fanny.
  B. She knows that events will have changed before Fanny gets her letter.
  C. She does not want to appear to tell Fanny what to do about marriage.
  D. She realizes that Fanny will ignore anything she says.

_____ 5. As social commentary, what does Austen accomplish in "On Making an Agreeable Marriage"?
  A. She consciously analyzes marriage customs of the period.
  B. She unconsciously depicts society's expectations for marriage.
  C. She consciously points out the flaws in how society treats women.
  D. She unconsciously criticizes how women allow themselves to be treated.

____ 6. What was Wollstonecraft's purpose in writing *A Vindication of the Rights of Woman?*

    A. to call attention how society has limited women's potential

    B. to complain about the lack of education she was given

    C. to criticize the education and intelligence of men

    D. to discourage women from rebelling against a social system

____ 7. To what does Wollstonecraft compare the minds of women in *A Vindication of the Rights of Woman?*

    A. the impression of being too frivolous to learn

    B. flowers that are planted in soil that is too rich

    C. men who have never had the benefits of education

    D. children before they go to school

____ 8. What does Wollstonecraft mean in *A Vindication of the Rights of Woman* when she says women should "become more masculine"?

    A. They should learn to compete with men as equals.

    B. They should try hard to make themselves beautiful.

    C. They should educate themselves and exercise their bodies.

    D. They should not hesitate to use their beauty to gain power.

Vocabulary and Grammar

____ 9. Which vocabulary word correctly completes this sentence?

    It took great _____ to speak out for women's rights as Mary Wollstonecraft did in the 1700s.

    A. scruples

    B. vindication

    C. fortitude

    D. gravity

____ 10. Which definition best fits the italicized vocabulary word in this sentence?

    Wollstonecraft compares women to flowers that at first appeal to a *fastidious* eye but lose their appeal as age makes their beauty fade.

    A. generous; willing

    B. thoughtful; wondering

    C. false; unearned

    D. particular; hard to please

___ **11.** In which sentence are commas in a series used *incorrectly?*

    A. Women were made to appear weak, dull, and useless due to social attitudes.

    B. With opportunities for education, they became intelligent, self-assured, and strong.

    C. They spent their time in dressing, making themselves up, and seeking husbands.

    D. Men did not appreciate their strengths, their abilities, and their judgment.

Essay

12. Based on "On Making an Agreeable Marriage," what can you conclude were some of the most important qualities that women should look for in a husband in the early 1800s? In an essay, mention these qualities and explain what Jane Austen thought of them.

13. In an essay, compare Austen's social commentary of "On Making an Agreeable Marriage" with Wollstonecraft's commentary in the excerpt from *A Vindication of the Rights of Woman* with regard to their being either conscious or unconscious. What are the assumptions the two writers make about social customs? Do they accept or challenge these assumptions? Use examples from both commentaries to support your response.

"On Making an Agreeable Marriage" by Jane Austen
from **A Vindication of the Rights of Woman** by Mary Wollstonecraft
Selection Test B

Critical Reading *Identify the letter of the choice that best completes the statement or answers the question.*

____ 1. Above all other considerations, Jane Austen felt that her niece should marry
   A. the eldest son of a wealthy man.
   B. a smart man.
   C. a man she respected.
   D. a man she liked.

____ 2. "On Making an Agreeable Marriage" might be read as a form of social commentary that
   A. criticizes society.
   B. criticizes a certain person.
   C. purposefully records society's foibles.
   D. unconsciously reflects social attitudes.

____ 3. Jane Austen's letter to her niece suggests that she hopes Fanny will
   A. never marry.
   B. marry well.
   C. go on as before.
   D. be cold to Mr. J. P.

____ 4. Mary Wollstonecraft wrote *A Vindication of the Rights of Woman* to
   A. complain about her lack of education.
   B. record the customs of the day.
   C. criticize society's view of women.
   D. criticize men.

____ 5. Mary Wollstonecraft's *A Vindication of the Rights of Woman* might be subtitled
   A. *A Demand for Understanding.*
   B. *A Plea for Better Education for Women.*
   C. *A Request for Equal Employment Opportunity for All.*
   D. *A Lament for the Sorrows of Women.*

____ 6. Mary Wollstonecraft compares women's minds to
   A. the minds of children.
   B. a mistake of nature.
   C. flowers planted in soil that is too rich.
   D. infertile soil.

____ 7. Wollstonecraft's purpose in writing *A Vindication of the Rights of Woman* was to
   A. persuade readers to accept her point of view.
   B. explain a social problem to readers.
   C. rally female readers to her cause.
   D. publish her thoughts on feminist philosophy.

____ 8. Which describes how the word *vindication* in the title of Mary Wollstonecraft's essay reflects her purpose for writing?
   A. *Vindication* means "placing blame"; Wollstonecraft wishes to criticize men for holding women back.
   B. *Vindication* means "justification"; Wollstonecraft is justifying why women should have equal rights.
   C. *Vindication* means "the state of being spiteful or critical"; Wollstonecraft is venting her frustration over the state of women's education.
   D. *Vindication* means "reasoned and well thought out"; Wollstonecraft wishes to explain a long history of poor treatment of women.

____ 9. At the time Jane Austen and Mary Wollstonecraft were writing, women's education tended to focus mainly on
   A. instruction in how to run a household.
   B. lessons taught by a governess.
   C. ladylike accomplishments.
   D. indoor pursuits.

Vocabulary and Grammar

____ 10. A person who behaves with *solicitude* is being _____.
   A. careful
   B. proper
   C. faithful
   D. thoughtful

____ 11. An *amiable* person is _____.
   A. antisocial
   B. friendly
   C. trusting
   D. happy

____ 12. If a seller makes a *specious* claim, that person is being _____.
   A. disloyal
   B. deceptive
   C. inappropriate
   D. unctuous

On the line, write the letter of the one best answer.

____ 13. In a series of three items, a final series comma comes
   A. immediately before the final noun.
   B. immediately after the final noun.
   C. immediately before the conjunction.
   D. immediately after the conjunction.

____ **14.** Which sentence uses serial commas correctly?

    A. Mary Wollstonecraft, Jane Austen, and, others wrote perceptively about the society of their time.

    B. Trust, and respect, and mutual affection were the qualities Jane Austen felt were necessary for an agreeable marriage.

    C. Mary Wollstonecraft thought that most women of her day were undereducated underchallenged, and underachieving.

    D. Austen wrote *Pride and Prejudice*, *Emma*, and *Sense and Sensibility*.

Essay

15. Jane Austen and Mary Wollstonecraft lived around the same time and shared many of the same ideas, although their writing styles differed radically. Write an essay that compares and contrasts the ideas in Austen's "On Making an Agreeable Marriage" with those in Wollstonecraft's *A Vindication of the Rights of Woman*.

16. When *A Vindication of the Rights of Woman* was first published, it caused great public outcry, not only because of its content but also because of its straightforward, blunt style. In those days people were not accustomed to women's speaking their minds. Write an essay that defines Wollstonecraft's style. Do you think her style would be considered blunt by today's standards?

Evaluate Literary Trends: Integrating Grammar Skills

Prewriting: Finding a Focus

Use the organizing chart below to help you evaluate the works you have read and the values celebrated by Romanticism, as well as their possible impact.

Work	Romantic Values	My Evaluation

Drafting: Organizing Your Essay

Use the elaborated outline format below to help you fill in details and examples for your essay.

    I. Topic Sentence:

        A. Examples:

            1. Specific Details:

            2. Specific Details:

        B. Examples:

            1. Specific Details:

            2. Specific Details:

    II. Topic Sentence:

        A. Examples:

            1. Specific Details:

            2. Specific Details:

        B. Examples:

            1. Specific Details:

            2. Specific Details:

   III. Topic Sentence:

        A. Examples:

            1. Specific Details:

            2. Specific Details:

        B. Examples:

            1. Specific Details:

            2. Specific Details:

Writing About Literature—Unit 4
Evaluate Literary Trends: Integrating Grammar Skills

Replacing Vague Language

Revise your draft to eliminate words that are vague or imprecise. Replace them with vivid, precise words that tell exactly what you mean.

Vague: Wordsworth likes nature because he can find out lots of things and feel really comfortable there.

Better: Wordsworth values nature as a source of wisdom and a spiritual home.

Revising to Replace Vague Language

DIRECTIONS: *Rewrite each sentence, replacing vague or imprecise words with vivid, precise ones.*

1. Parts of the French Revolution made the Romantics interested in things related to the common people.

   _____

   _____

2. Problems caused by industrialization made the Romantics not interested in science and reason.

   _____

   _____

3. The Romantics believed that things about nature could help people.

   _____

   _____

4. The Romantics liked things like simplicity, emotion, and individuality.

   _____

   _____

5. The Romantics were interested in fantasy and reality, and they believed in imagination.

   _____

   _____

6. The Romantics believed people could discover things about life, not through stuff like science, but by using different parts of their brains.

   _____

   _____

Name _____ Date _____

Workplace Writing: Job Portfolio and Résumé

Prewriting: Gathering Facts

Complete the graphic organizer below to compile information about yourself for your résumé.

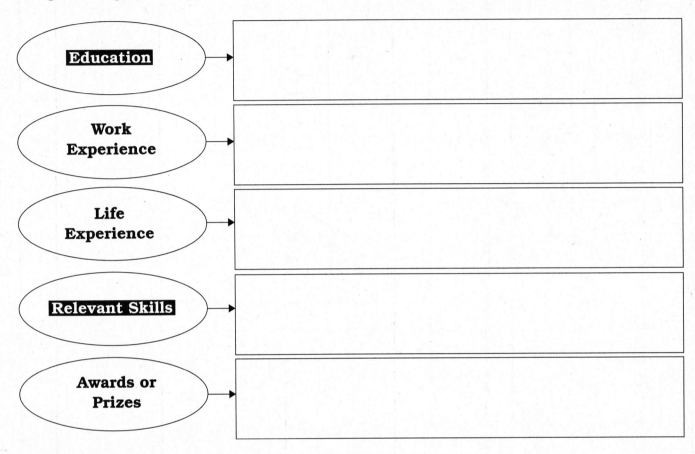

Drafting: Shaping Your Résumé

Outline your résumé below by choosing and organizing clear headings on the left and listing the experiences you want to include in your résumé on the right.

Headings	My Experiences

Writing Workshop—Unit4
Job Portfolio and Résumé: Integrating Grammar Skills

Active vs. Passive Voice

In a résumé, your language should project a tone of all-around competence and initiative. In every part of your résumé, present yourself as an active, take-charge employee who seizes opportunities to make effective contributions to the workplace team. One way you can do this is through the words you choose. Use verbs in the **active voice**, rather than the passive. Tell what you *do*, rather than what *is done* by you.

> **Don't use passive voice:**   I *am assigned* to operate a cash register.
>
> **Use active voice:**   I *operate* a cash register.

Identifying Active and Passive Voice

A. DIRECTIONS: *Write* active *or* passive *to identify the type of verb used in each sentence.*

____ 1. I train and manage servers in a fast-food restaurant.

____ 2. I am required to write feature stories for a school newspaper.

____ 3. I am allowed to teach two karate classes per week.

____ 4. I plan and create posters for school events.

____ 5. I answer the phone and take messages at a YMCA office.

Changing Passive Voice to Active Voice

B. DIRECTIONS: *Rewrite each sentence, changing the verbs from passive voice to active voice.*

1. I am allowed to assist the coach of a middle-school football team.

   _____

2. I am supposed to recruit and train tutors for an after-school study club.

   _____

3. I was trained to make donuts for a local bakery.

   _____

4. I am required to assist customers in a shoe store.

   _____

5. I am assigned to take phone orders at a pizza shop.

Name _____ Date _____

Proofreading Practice

DIRECTIONS: *Proofread the following passage, looking for 26 misspelled words. Cross out each misspelled word, and write it correctly in the space above.*

One of the most fameous composers of the Romantic era was Frédéric Chopin (1810–1849), a pianist of French and Polish heritage. Chopin wrote very few compositions for orchestra. Rather than creating simphonic works, he concentrated on writeing for the piano. His works for piano demonstrate a startleing originalety and a pasionate intensity that make them universally appealing.

Very early in life, Chopin's prodigeous talent was recognised. When he was only seven, his first composition for piano was published. His vivid impressions of Polish folk music were reflected in some of his early pieces, which showed a relianse on traditional folk rhythms. At age sixteen, Chopin entered the Warsaw Conservatory of Music. The teacher runing that school knew that Chopin was a natural marvle whose talent should not be hemed in by too much academic training.

Chopin aspyred to greatness, and to help him succede, his family sent him to study and perform in Vienna. There, he began writing his études, or exercizes, designed to help pianists develop the flexibilaty they needed to master the novle fingering techniques of his compositions.

In 1830, Chopin proceded to Paris, the center of European culture and hotbed of Romantic composers. At first, he experienced some profesional problems there, and he realised that some people were suspicious of his style of piano music. Soon, though, his work was appreciated for its creativity and its appeal to the scences.

Chopin gained some notoriety for his romantic relationship with the a young woman named Aurore Dudevant, who took the pseudonim George Sand as a novelist. Although his health became precareous at this time, he managed to create a succession of dareingly original masterpieces, despite the time and energy he consumed in socializing with George Sand and her friends.

After his death in 1849, Chopin was criticised because his work did not fit the accepted academic standards of the time. However, the expresiveness and passion of his music have made him an eternal favorite with music lovers of all ages.

Critiquing Persuasive Devices

After choosing a persuasive speech, fill out the following chart to help you evaluate the speaker's use of persuasive devices.

Topic of speech: _____

What is the main purpose of the speech?
What evidence is presented?
What fallacious arguments are used?
What effective rhetorical devices are used?
Which persuasive devices used were most effective? Why?

Suggestions for Further Reading—Unit 4

DIRECTIONS: *Think about the books you have read. Then, on a separate piece of paper, answer the discussion questions and take notes for your literature circle.*

Emma by Jane Austen

Discussion Emma is a character who has imagination and determination, but lacks self-awareness. Write a paragraph explaining how Emma comes to understand herself better by the novel's end. Has she outgrown some of her weaknesses or not?

Connections—Literature Circle Consider the pairing of Emma and George, Jane and Frank, and Harriet and Robert. How do you feel about each of these three marriages? Do you think they will be good partnerships or not? Give reasons for your assessments.

Pride and Prejudice by Jane Austen

Discussion Jane Austen is a master of irony. In her writing, she has a keen ability to point out the disparities between appearances and reality. Think of some of the examples of irony in *Pride and Prejudice.* Name one that was most effective for you as a reader, and explain why. Did Austen use the irony to define a character, to make an observation about society, or both?

Connections—Literature Circle One of the themes of *Pride and Prejudice* is appearances, and their importance in genteel English society. Would Jane Austen find today's society similarly preoccupied with appearances? What would some of the differences and some of the similarities be between our world and Jane Austen's world?

Ivanhoe by Sir Walter Scott

Discussion Based on your reading of *Ivanhoe,* write a brief biography of the Templar. What were his reasons were for becoming a templar? How did he conduct himself during the Crusades? What led to his death? Was he a typical heroic figure? Describe his character as well as his actions.

Connections—Literature Circle Sir Walter Scott was interested in chivalry and medieval times. What do you think explains the attraction that the Romantics and Victorians had for past times? Do you think that modern society has similar longings?

Frankenstein by Mary Shelley

Discussion The inhuman behavior of people toward one another in one of the themes of *Frankenstein.* Think of some examples of inhumanity from the novel. Is Mary Shelley perhaps saying that there is a monstrous element in all of us? What do you think about this idea?

Connections—Literature Circle Victor's final advice to Walton is, "Seek happiness in tranquility and avoid ambition." Has ambition been the root of the evil in the story? If not, then what has been? Support your opinions with examples from the book.

Unit 4: Rebels and Dreamers
Benchmark Test 8

MULTIPLE CHOICE

Literary Analysis and Reading Skills *Read this selection from "Happy Insensibility" by John Keats. Then, answer the questions that follow.*

1 In a drear-nighted December,
2 Too happy, happy brook,
3 Thy bubblings ne'er remember
4 Apollo's summer look;
5 But with a sweet forgetting
6 They stay their crystal fretting,
7 Never, never petting
8 About the frozen time.

9 Ah! would 'twere so with many
10 A gentle girl and boy!
11 But were there ever any
12 Writhed not at passèd joy?
13 To know the change and feel it,
14 When there is none to heal it
15 Nor numbèd sense to steal it—
16 Was never said in rhyme.

1. Which of the following best paraphrases lines 1–8?
   A. Streams cannot be sad about winter because they do not remember summer.
   B. Streams are surprisingly emotional, even in winter.
   C. Streams bubble with happiness because they have the look of Apollo.
   D. If streams were people, they would be forgetful and insensitive.

2. What is the effect of the repetition of the word *happy* in lines 2 and 10?
   A. It emphasizes the joyous spirit of the speaker.
   B. It conveys that the tree and brook are overly happy with their condition.
   C. It makes the sound of a tree blowing in the cold wind.
   D. It highlights the main consonants used in the poem.

3. What question might you ask to help you understand this poem?
   A. How does a crystal look under a microscope?
   B. Where was the poet born?
   C. Why are most children unhappy?
   D. Who was Apollo?

4. How do the images of cold and wintertime convey the poet's theme?
   A. They contrast with the emotions of a child.
   B. They reflect the same changes as those in young people.
   C. They distract from the numbness of children.
   D. They create the setting where all children long to go.

5. Which of the following is characteristic of an ode?
   A. unrealistic imagery
   B. ridicule of the subject matter
   C. a lack of sound devices
   D. heightened emotion

6. Which of the following images might a poet use to convey the sublime?
   A. a troubled young person
   B. a favorite pet
   C. a star-filled night sky
   D. a broken tree branch

7. A poet who describes a feeling of bitterness as "an angry guest" is using which of the following?
   A. personification
   B. simile
   C. assonance
   D. internal rhyme

8. Which of the following defines the poetic device of *consonance*?
   A. the combination of consonant sounds at the ends of words
   B. the repetition of vowel sounds within words close to each other
   C. the repetition of consonant sounds in emphasized syllables
   D. the use of rhyme within, rather than at the end of, poetic lines

9. What is a good way to respond to the imagery in a poem?
   A. Imagine the poem without the imagery.
   B. Think of your associations with the imagery.
   C. Ignore the imagery in order to get at the poem's core meaning.
   D. Critique the poem's weaknesses.

10. Why is it important to analyze poetic effects, such as sound devices, in poetry?
   A. to enhance your comprehension
   B. to identify poetic effects
   C. to increase your appreciation
   D. to study the history of poetry

Read the selection. Then, answer the questions that follow.

   All men will grant that the happiness of the human species is the most desirable object for human science to promote; and that intellectual and moral happiness or pleasure is extremely to be preferred to those which are precarious and transitory. The methods which may be proposed for the attainment of this object, are various. If it could be proved that a sound political institution was of all others the most powerful engine for promoting individual good, or on the other hand that an erroneous and corrupt government was the most formidable adversary to the improvement of the species, it would follow that politics was the first and most important subject of human investigation.

   from *Of the Importance of Political Institutions* by William Godwin

11. What assumptions about society does the selection reveal?
   A. Political institutions should promote human happiness.
   B. Many different methods of government are appropriate.
   C. Individual freedom is more important than social harmony.
   D. Aristocrats are more capable in handling government business.

12. Why might the selection be described as political commentary?
    A. It uses persuasive devices.
    B. It offers opinions on political issues.
    C. It presents one political preference.
    D. It supports one type of political institution.

13. What can you do before reading to help you engage the material better?
    A. Ask someone to read it to you.
    B. Assume that the author is not serious.
    C. Discuss ideas for a paper on the topic.
    D. Consider what you know about the topic.

Read the selection. Then, answer the questions that follow.

It may fairly be questioned, whether government be not still more considerable in its incidental effects, than in those intended to be produced. Vice, for example, depends for its existence upon the existence of temptation. May not a good government strongly tend to extirpate [remove], and a bad one to increase the mass of temptation? Again, vice depends for its existence upon the existence of error. May not a good government by taking away all restraints upon the enquiring mind hasten, and a bad one by its patronage of error procrastinate the discovery and establishment of truth?

from *Of the Importance of Political Institutions* by William Godwin

14. What argument does the author make about the existence of temptation in society?
    A. The majority of people are tempted to do evil, regardless of the type of government.
    B. Poor governments increase temptations to break the law.
    C. When governments procrastinate, they lead citizens into criminal activities.
    D. A government must be strong enough to control the activities of all its citizens.

15. Which of the following is most likely to be the subject of a social commentary?
    A. weather patterns in parts of the country
    B. treatment of children in the workplace
    C. entertainment personality updates
    D. highlights from sporting events

16. What type of persuasive device is the following?

    Do you think you can save the whole world from starvation in the next year?

    A. rhetorical question
    B. balanced statement
    C. logical appeal
    D. factual reasoning

Vocabulary

17. Based on your knowledge of the Latin suffix -age, what does the word *pilgrimage* mean?
    A. condition of age
    B. settling in America
    C. state of being imprisoned
    D. journey to a sacred place

18. If you are an *impulsive* shopper, what do you often do when you are in a store?
    A. ask other people's advice about buying things
    B. buy things on the spur of the moment
    C. shop only on rare occasions
    D. take lots of time to consider each purchase

19. If the food at a picnic is *plenteous*, which of the following is true?
    A. There may not be enough food.
    B. There is more than enough food.
    C. The food is attracting insects.
    D. The food does not taste good.

20. Which of the following materials is *porous*?
    A. a kitchen sponge
    B. a wall clock
    C. a light bulb
    D. a ceiling fan

21. Based on the meaning of the root word -*journ*-, which of the following offers the best description of a *sojourn*?
    A. a time of rest
    B. an essay
    C. travel abroad
    D. a guidebook

22. If you have just *adjourned* a meeting, what will most of the people in the room do?
    A. raise their hands with questions
    B. quiet down and listen to you
    C. tell you whether or not they can attend
    D. get up and leave the room

23. Based on the meaning of the Latin root -*dec*-, how are the individuals in a *decile* divided?
    A. into groups of 5
    B. into groups of 10
    C. into groups of 50
    D. into groups of 100

24. Based on the meaning of the Latin root *-fort-*, what kind of a structure is a *fortification*?
    A. small and delicate
    B. elaborate and elegant
    C. strong and secure
    D. artistic and creative

Grammar

25. In which of the following sentences is a term of direct address correctly punctuated?
    A. My son, you darling boy, please, do not hurt anyone's feelings.
    B. My son, you darling boy please do not hurt anyone's feelings.
    C. My son, you darling boy, please do not hurt anyone's feelings.
    D. My son you darling boy, please do not hurt anyone's feelings.

26. Where should comma(s) be placed in the following sentence?

    To you my leader I pledge my loyalty.

    A. after *you*
    B. after *you* and *leader*
    C. after *leader*
    D. after *leader* and *pledge*

27. Based on the grammar in the following sentence, what can you assume?

    If you were to own the whole city, I would still want to live somewhere else.

    A. the speaker likes living in the city
    B. the speaker has a house in another place
    C. the person referred to is very wealthy
    D. the person referred to will never own the whole city

28. Which of the following sentences has an error in subject-verb agreement?
    A. To encourage my child to eat her breakfast, I am serving fruit.
    B. The author's prediction about the books sales were correct.
    C. Under the table, the small kitten was shaking with fear.
    D. If you cannot do the job, I will hire someone else.

29. What type of subject-verb agreement error is contained in the following sentence?

    Yesterday, the neighbor's puppies are climbing all over my vegetable garden.

    A. tense
    B. number
    C. linking verb
    D. pronoun

30. What is the subject of the following sentence?

    And happy as a bird in spring, to the nearby park I went.

    A. bird
    B. spring
    C. park
    D. I

31. Which of the following sentences uses correlative conjunctions correctly?
    A. Neither Peter or Micah wanted to attend the dinner play.
    B. Both Lara, Sharita, and Danielle jumped into the water immediately.
    C. Not only did I want to get away, but I also wanted to stay away.
    D. Just as my grandmother earned a college degree, I also plan to as well.

32. Where should comma(s) be placed in the following sentence?

    The delightful young child longed for his home his books and his old friends.

    A. after *delightful*
    B. after *young*
    C. after *home* and *books*
    D. after *books*

ESSAY

33. You know that symbols are often used in poetry because they are a physical way of representing something non-physical. Suppose that you are planning to write a poem on feeling disconnected or apart from other people. Record at least three images that might convey that feeling. For each image, write two or three sensory details to accompany the image.

34. Create a fictional character and write a monologue for the character that conveys your views on the jobs that are available to teenagers. Consider the qualities your character will have. Then write a monologue that uses dramatic effects to make your point.

35. You are assigned to write an introduction to one of the poems on this test. Make a list of five questions you would use to guide your research on the poem's background.

36. What political issues seem most important to people you know? Write an editorial on one of these issues, reporting your facts clearly. Use forceful, persuasive language to convey your message.

37. Have you ever disagreed with a critical review? Select a few comments that you disagree with from a review of a book you have read or a movie you have seen. Then, write a letter to the writer of the review in which you explain what you disagree with and why. Make your argument convincing by supporting it with specific details.

ANSWERS

Diagnostic Test 7, p. 2

MULTIPLE CHOICE

1. ANS: D
2. ANS: B
3. ANS: A
4. ANS: B
5. ANS: D
6. ANS: C
7. ANS: C
8. ANS: A
9. ANS: B
10. ANS: B
11. ANS: A
12. ANS: B
13. ANS: C
14. ANS: A
15. ANS: B

Unit 4 Introduction

Names and Terms to Know, p. 5

A. 1. D; 2. G; 3. H; 4. C; 5. A; 6. F; 7. B; 8. E

B. Sample Answers

1. The Jacobin leadership during the Reign of Terror was headed by Maximilien de Robespierre.
2. The Whig victory in the election of 1830 led to the passage of the Reform Bill of 1832, which gave the vote to the small but important middle class.
3. Romantic writers generally protested against the misery and ugliness that resulted from industrialization.
4. Jean-Jacques Rousseau's ideas influenced both American and French revolutionaries.

Focus Questions, p. 6

Sample Answers

1. Most British intellectuals favored the democratic ideals of the French Revolution in its early phase. Later, however, British public opinion was shocked by the violence of the Reign of Terror. Conservative Tories in Britain choked off hopes for reform and suspended certain basic liberties.
2. Problems included overcrowded factory towns, unpleasant and unsafe working conditions in the factories, and long working hours for low pay. As symbolized by the Peterloo Massacre of 1819, British society seemed fractured between the working class, which demanded reform, and the upper class, which fiercely resisted it. After the Whig victory in the election of 1830, the first law governing factory safety was passed by Parliament in 1833.
3. Wordsworth and Coleridge favored scenes from nature and common, everyday life, as well as subjects that could be linked with the workings of the human imagination. The second generation of Romantics reacted rebelliously toward British conservatism: Byron and Shelley, for example, advocated radical politics.

"To a Mouse" and "To a Louse" by Robert Burns
"Woo'd and Married and A'" by Joanna Baillie

Vocabulary Warm-up Exercises, p. 8

A. 1. notion
2. compared
3. companion
4. trouble
5. impudence
6. social
7. schemes
8. union

B. Sample Answers

1. F; *Dearest* means "most valuable," so your *dearest* possession is what you value most.
2. F; *Grieve* means "to mourn," so you would be more likely to cry than laugh when you *grieve*.
3. T; A *pouch* is a "small bag for carrying things."
4. T; An uncovered arm is indeed *bare*, which refers to something that is naked.
5. T; *Patient* means "being willing to wait for something," and this is what you need to take the time to grow plants.
6. F; *Bashfully* means "timidly," which is not the way you should behave if you want to get noticed.
7. T; *Waste* means "things that have been destroyed or are no longer useful," so a dump would be filled with piles of such things.
8. T; *Prospects* means "possibilities," and you need to look at these to make the right choice.

Reading Warm-up A, p. 9

Sample Answers

1. It was a movement that lasted a long time; A *notion* is an idea formed on an impulse or a whim.
2. (ideas of order, calm, and balance, and rejection of nature); A young man with a boring *social* life might go out to movies with a group of friends.
3. the Romantics held very specific views about nature and the individual; *Compared* means "examined to note similarities."
4. (people with nature); Students might form a *union* to try to get the dress code changed.
5. did not have respect for; The child was sent to his room for showing *impudence* to his parents.
6. (problem); One kind of *trouble* some modern societies have is racism.

7. <u>many problems would disappear</u>; One career that involves coming up with *schemes* is marketing.

8. (peer); My traveling *companion* is my sister.

Reading Warm-up B, p. 10

Sample Answers

1. <u>a book of poetry and a sandwich</u>; A *pouch* is a small bag used for carrying things.

2. <u>made himself comfortable</u>; *Bare* ground would not have anything growing on it; it would simply be dirt.

3. (reading); A phrase that means about the same as *dearest* is "most loved."

4. (waiting so quietly); A small child might have trouble being *patient* while waiting to have cake at a birthday party.

5. <u>Throwing away his leftovers</u>; *Waste* means "something that is ruined or made useless."

6. (chances); The talented engineer had evaluated many business *prospects*.

7. <u>that mean bird missing out on the rest of the bread</u>; Most people would <u>grieve</u> for the death of someone close to them.

8. (timidly); A person who is behaving *bashfully* looks shy; he or she might blush or look down at the floor.

Literary Analysis: Dialect, p. 11

Possible Responses

1. "Little, sleek, cowering, timorous beast"; by using dialect to address the mouse, the speaker achieves a friendly and affectionate tone.

2. "An occasional ear of grain in a bundle / Is a small request"; the use of expressions familiar to a Scottish farmer stresses the strong bond that exists between the land and all creatures.

3. "And nothing, now, to build a new one"; dialect effectively expresses the speaker's tenderness toward the mouse's plight.

4. "To withstand the winter's sleety drizzle/ And cold frost"; using the harsh sounding words *cranreuch cauld* emphasizes the speaker's strong empathy for the mouse.

Reading Strategy: Translate Dialect, p. 12

1. run—context ("an' chase")

2. at times—reading the footnote

3. house—look for similarities with a standard English word

4. leave—noting that the apostrophe stands for the omitted *v*

Vocabulary Builder, p. 13

A. Sample Responses

1. Making tired or bored

2. Arousing disgust or loathing

3. Bothering or irritating

B. 1. discretion; 2. impudence; 3. inconstantly; 4. dominion; 5. winsome

Grammar and Style: Interjections, p. 14

A. 1. My gosh!; 2. Hey!; 3. Good grief!; 4. Aha!; 5. Yikes!; 6. Whew!

B. Sample Responses

1. Well! Now the dentist wants to fill three of my teeth.

2. Hurrah! The team will compete in the playoffs!

3. Hey! I don't see why I should wash the dishes when it is your turn.

4. Alas! Many died during the famine.

5. Whoa! Where are you going with my car keys?

6. Oh! I forgot Margo's birthday.

7. My goodness! I didn't study for the test!

Enrichment: Social Studies, p. 17

Suggested Responses

1. Students should identify the language as the Scottish dialect of English, and they should identify articles of clothing from the poems, such as: bonnet with fatt'rels, flannen toy, wyliecoat, Lunardi, pearlins, purfles. Students will have to do research to find out about the music and food of Scotland.

2. Students should choose one American culture with which they are familiar, and note the language or dialect, clothing, music, and food that are characteristic of it. For example, a student who chooses to describe the Athabascan culture of the interior of Alaska might mention a dialect of Athabascan, clothing such as mukluks and parkas, traditional instruments such as drums, and food such as smoked salmon.

Selection Test A, p. 18

Critical Reading

1. ANS: B	DIF: Easy		OBJ: Comprehension
2. ANS: C	DIF: Easy		OBJ: Literary Analysis
3. ANS: A	DIF: Easy		OBJ: Reading Strategy
4. ANS: D	DIF: Easy		OBJ: Interpretation
5. ANS: B	DIF: Easy		OBJ: Interpretation
6. ANS: B	DIF: Easy		OBJ: Literary Analysis
7. ANS: D	DIF: Easy		OBJ: Reading Strategy
8. ANS: C	DIF: Easy		OBJ: Comprehension
9. ANS: A	DIF: Easy		OBJ: Reading Strategy
10. ANS: B	DIF: Easy		OBJ: Comprehension

Vocabulary and Grammar

11. ANS: A	DIF: Easy		OBJ: Vocabulary
12. ANS: D	DIF: Easy		OBJ: Grammar

Essay

13. Students should mention that the bride is, at first, upset and crying. She is getting married, but she is poor and does not have fine clothing to wear. The mother tries to comfort her by telling her to be practical and work hard. Then the wealth she gains will be more valuable and lasting than any that might be given to her. The bride's attitude then changes as she realizes that love is enough to have when starting a marriage.

Difficulty: *Easy*

Objective: *Essay*

14. Students may respond that the dialect makes the poem more interesting and fun to read because it is enjoyable to pronounce the dialect, which contributes rhythm to the poem. Students will generally also say that the dialect makes the poem more difficult because many of the words are unfamiliar.

Difficulty: *Easy*

Objective: *Essay*

Selection Test B, p. 21

Critical Reading

1. ANS: C	DIF: Easy	OBJ: Literary Analysis
2. ANS: A	DIF: Average	OBJ: Interpretation
3. ANS: B	DIF: Average	OBJ: Interpretation
4. ANS: D	DIF: Average	OBJ: Literary Analysis
5. ANS: B	DIF: Average	OBJ: Reading Strategy
6. ANS: C	DIF: Easy	OBJ: Reading Strategy
7. ANS: B	DIF: Easy	OBJ: Comprehension
8. ANS: A	DIF: Average	OBJ: Comprehension
9. ANS: A	DIF: Average	OBJ: Interpretation
10. ANS: C	DIF: Average	OBJ: Literary Analysis
11. ANS: D	DIF: Average	OBJ: Reading Strategy

Vocabulary and Grammar

12. ANS: A	DIF: Average	OBJ: Vocabulary
13. ANS: D	DIF: Easy	OBJ: Vocabulary
14. ANS: B	DIF: Easy	OBJ: Vocabulary
15. ANS: C	DIF: Average	OBJ: Grammar
16. ANS: C	DIF: Average	OBJ: Grammar

Essay

17. Students' essays should identify strong similarities in the three poems. For example, all are written about everyday subjects and use conversational language that contains a strong Scottish dialect. Both poets use clear rhyme schemes, dialogue, and direct address.

Difficulty: *Average*

Objective: *Essay*

18. Students' essays should identify characteristics that might have made Burns's poetry popular in Scotland.

For example, students might point out that the use of Scottish dialect could give readers the sense that Burns understood the lives of uneducated workers. The image of a farmer plowing in the fall might be familiar to many. Lice would have been familiar to all Scots of Burns's day, and the theme of "To a Louse," which declares that all people are the same, probably touched a common chord in his readers.

Difficulty: *Challenging*

Objective: *Essay*

"The Lamb," "The Tyger," and "The Chimney Sweeper," "Infant Sorrow" by William Blake

Vocabulary Warm-up Exercises, p. 25

A. 1. mild
2. mead
3. struggling
4. bound
5. seize
6. wept
7. rejoice
8. aspire

B. Sample Answers

1. An <u>immortal</u> character in a story is one who cannot die.
2. A <u>meek</u> person is very shy.
3. If something is <u>distant</u>, it is far away.
4. Injured <u>sinews</u> would prevent an athlete from doing gymnastics.
5. If you <u>grasp</u> a ball, it will not bounce away.
6. If you <u>sulk</u> about something, it means that you are very unhappy about it.
7. One example of a <u>dread</u> noise is the sound of a tornado approaching.
8. A person working out in a gym all day is clearly <u>striving</u> to achieve his fitness goals.

Reading Warm-up A, p. 26

Sample Answers

1. <u>opportunities to explore their potential</u>; A word that means the same as *seize* is *grab*.
2. <u>to achieve their creative goals</u>; I *aspire* to own my own construction company one day.
3. (with difficulty); The salmon were *struggling* to swim upstream against the river's current.
4. (tears); My mother *wept* for joy at my sister's wedding.
5. (joy); Someone might *rejoice* about getting a great new job.
6. <u>a peaceful meadow</u>; Children might play tag or fly a kite in a *mead*.
7. (gentle); A word that means the opposite of *mild* is *harsh*.
8. <u>by heavy chains</u>; *Bound* means "tied" or "held tightly together."

Reading Warm-up B, p. 27

1. to combine art with poetry; A synonym for *striving* is *longing*.

2. that he had an artistic ability that needed to be developed; *Grasp* in this sentence means "to understand" or "to grab an idea."

3. (shy); A person who is *meek* acts shy, perhaps speaking very softly or refusing to meet other people's eyes.

4. The process took a great deal of muscle work; A swimmer with injured *sinews* would probably not be able to swim for quite awhile.

5. (poverty); A word that means about the same as *dread* is *awful*.

6. During his life, Blake's poetry was not popular; The *distant* buildings gradually seemed to grow taller and larger as we neared the city.

7. (worrying and pouting); When they *sulk,* people usually stick out their lower lips and look pouty and unhappy.

8. (it will never die); The Greek god Zeus is *immortal.*

Literary Analysis: Symbols, p. 28

1. *Meaning:* Jesus Christ
   Source: Bible

2. *Meaning:* Jesus Christ
   Source: Bible

3. *Meaning:* the Baby Jesus
   Source: Bible

4. *Meaning:* innocent
   Source: Bible

5. *Meaning:* place where human fates are created
   Source: Norse mythology

6. *Meaning:* messenger
   Source: Bible

Reading Strategy: Use Visuals as a Key to Meaning, p. 29

Sample Answers

2. "The Tyger"—The tyger appears solitary and fearsome, and it lives in a dark wood. This image supports the poem's description of the "fearful symmetry" of the tyger.

3. "The Chimney Sweeper"—The children in the illustration look miserable. The setting is dark and the mood is tragic. The chimney sweeps in the poem live miserable lives.

4. "Infant Sorrow"—The scene depicted in the illustration would be a perfect example of the "dangerous world" described in the poem.

Vocabulary Builder, p. 30

A. Sample Answers

1. is full of life

2. felt a loss of spirit or energy

3. waited to see what would come to be, or arise

4. came to an end

5. has an impact on the reader's life

B. 1. B; 2. A; 3. C

C. 1. vales; 2. symmetry; 3. aspire

Grammar and Style: *Rise* and *Raise*, p. 31

A. 2. risen (*rise:* past participle)

3. raised (*raise:* past tense)

4. rise (*rise:* present infinitive)

B. 1. The sun rises over the far horizon.

2. We rose and gathered up our camp equipment.

3. Abigail and John had raised the kayak onto the roof of the car.

4. I watched as morning mist rose from the nearby river.

Enrichment: Fine Art, p. 34

Sample Responses

1. The illustrations are simple and illustrate the main subject of each poem. For example, the lambs in the illustration are meek and docile and eat from the hand of the boy. The tiger is solitary and the setting in which it lives is wild and untamed, much like the "forests of the night" described in the poem.

2. The illustration accompanying "The Lamb" depicts a peaceable and calm setting. Harmony is symbolized in the meeting of the branches at the top of the illustration. On the other hand, the illustration for "The Tyger" shows a dark and wooded setting. The tiger is alone, its eyes fiery and powerful. The lamb and the tiger are presented as opposites in these two illustrations.

3. The illustrations, like the poetry itself, focus on nature and "the common people." In both illustrations the poetry is framed by foliage. The pastoral scene of "The Lamb" depicts a common setting used by many of the Romantic poets.

Selection Test A, p. 35

Critical Reading

1. ANS: B	DIF: Easy	OBJ: Comprehension
2. ANS: A	DIF: Easy	OBJ: Interpretation
3. ANS: A	DIF: Easy	OBJ: Literary Analysis
4. ANS: B	DIF: Easy	OBJ: Literary Analysis
5. ANS: C	DIF: Easy	OBJ: Literary Analysis
6. ANS: A	DIF: Easy	OBJ: Reading Strategy
7. ANS: D	DIF: Easy	OBJ: Comprehension
8. ANS: C	DIF: Easy	OBJ: Comprehension
9. ANS: A	DIF: Easy	OBJ: Comprehension

Vocabulary and Grammar

10. ANS: C	DIF: Easy	OBJ: Vocabulary
11. ANS: A	DIF: Easy	OBJ: Vocabulary

12. ANS: B DIF: Easy OBJ: Grammar

Essay

13. Students should recognize that this line is basically asking the question, Did God who made gentle, harmless animals like lambs also make ferocious animals like the tiger? Students should see that this question recalls the question that opens "The Lamb": "Little Lamb who made thee." The answer that Blake appears to want is that the same Creator who made the Lamb also made the Tyger.
Difficulty: *Easy*
Objective: *Essay*

14. Students should note that William Blake sympathized with the chimney sweepers. The speaker in "The Chimney Sweeper" tells a sorrowful story. His mother died while he was young, and his father sold him to become a chimney sweeper. He was so young, he scarcely could talk. His friend Tom Dacre had his head shaved and he dreams of coffins filled with his friends. Altogether, it is a gloomy picture, and Blake's attitude seems to be one of sympathy.
Difficulty: *Easy*
Objective: *Essay*

Selection Test B, p. 38

Critical Reading

1. ANS: C	DIF: Challenging	OBJ: Literary Analysis
2. ANS: D	DIF: Average	OBJ: Interpretation
3. ANS: A	DIF: Average	OBJ: Comprehension
4. ANS: D	DIF: Challenging	OBJ: Reading Strategy
5. ANS: A	DIF: Easy	OBJ: Interpretation
6. ANS: B	DIF: Easy	OBJ: Reading Strategy
7. ANS: C	DIF: Easy	OBJ: Comprehension
8. ANS: C	DIF: Average	OBJ: Literary Analysis
9. ANS: D	DIF: Easy	OBJ: Literary Analysis
10. ANS: C	DIF: Easy	OBJ: Interpretation
11. ANS: A	DIF: Average	OBJ: Comprehension
12. ANS: B	DIF: Average	OBJ: Reading Strategy

Vocabulary and Grammar

13. ANS: C	DIF: Average	OBJ: Vocabulary
14. ANS: D	DIF: Easy	OBJ: Vocabulary
15. ANS: B	DIF: Average	OBJ: Grammar
16. ANS: C	DIF: Average	OBJ: Grammar

Essay

17. Students should present their interpretations and comparisons of "The Lamb" and "The Tyger" supported by specific details from the poems. For example, they may say that the lamb and the tyger symbolize the opposite sides of human nature and of human experience. Also, students might say that the peaceful streams and vales in which the lamb lives stand opposite the dark and chaotic wood in which the tyger lives. Students may also mention that although the lamb and the tyger are set up as opposites, there is a similarity between them. According to Blake, they were both made by the Creator.
Difficulty: *Average*
Objective: *Essay*

18. Students should make their interpretations using examples from the two poems they chose to support their ideas. Students may mention that the lamb symbolizes not only innocence, but also the Creator. They might also mention that the tiger represents experience and worldliness. In the cases of both "The Lamb" and "The Tyger," students might mention the significance of the settings described in each poem. If students choose "The Chimney Sweeper" or "Infant Sorrow," they might mention the symbols of heaven and the creator in "The Chimney Sweeper" and the symbol of confinement in "Infant Sorrow."
Difficulty: *Challenging*
Objective: *Essay*

From the Scholar's Desk

Elizabeth McCracken Introduces "Introduction" to *Frankenstein* by Mary Shelley, p. 41

1. When she was seven years old, McCracken dreamed of a monster who was half-human and half-robot, with bolts on his neck and a flashing ambulance light on the top of his head.

2. A. She means the mysterious attraction that horror holds for human beings.
   B. Answers will vary, but many students will agree with McCracken. Encourage students to support their explanations with reasons and examples.

3. The dream came from her own brain, and her "dream-self" wanted to return to it.

4. She wanted to make up people and then wonder where they came from.

5. Answers will vary. Sample questions: How does the monster in Mary Shelley's *Frankenstein* compare with the monster in McCracken's dream? Does Mary Shelley offer any clues to the riddle of why horror stories fascinate so many people?

Elizabeth McCracken

Listening and Viewing, p. 42

Sample answers and guidelines for evaluation:

Segment 1: Elizabeth McCracken uses her experiences with her eccentric family, who told her very odd, interesting stories when she was growing up as the basis for her fiction characters. Students may suggest that it is easier to write about a real person or an occurrence to create fiction rather than invent an entire story.

Segment 2: *Frankenstein* is a gothic novel because it explores the dark, frightening side of human nature. Students may suggest that the character of Victor Frankenstein is motivated by his emotion and humanity, which are universal as well as timeless and are just as significant in today's world as they were almost 200 years ago.

Segment 3: Elizabeth McCracken develops her characters so that she knows them well enough to predict what they are capable of doing in the plot of her book. Students may suggest that in order to make your story believable a writer must be willing to shape the plot around the actions that a character would be likely to perform.

Segment 4: She advises young people to write the kind of story they want to read and to write to entertain themselves. Students may agree that if you write a story that you would enjoy you will do a better job constructing it, while other students may feel that it makes no difference whether it is the type of book you would read, and that instead writing relies on skill.

Introduction to Frankenstein
by Mary Wollstonecraft Shelley

Vocabulary Warm-up Exercises, p. 44

A. 1. devout
   2. furnish
   3. acceded
   4. endeavor
   5. successively
   6. contrive
   7. adorns
   8. incitement

B. Sample Answers
   1. F; *Odious* means "horrible," so if something is *odious*, people would not like it.
   2. F; *Appendage* means "something added on," but a tree trunk is the main part of the tree.
   3. T; *Bestow* means "to present as a gift."
   4. F; A *platitude* is a statement lacking in originality.
   5. T; *Comply* means "obey," and it is important to comply with such rules for safety.
   6. T; *Illustrious* means "well-known," and many people can identify athletes.
   7. T; *Relinquished* means "let go of."
   8. F; *Incessant* means "constant," so a quiet library would not be a place of constant noise.

Reading Warm-up A, p. 45
Sample Answers
   1. (sincere); Gail is a *devout* fan of Japanese animation.

2. the belief that she would realize the great potential that her father believed she had; A synonym for as *furnish* is *provide*.
3. (encouragement); *Incitement* means "encouragement" or "urging."
4. (task); An *endeavor* I might like to try some day is learning to play the piano.
5. Percy suggested that they should each contrive to write a horror story; *Contrive* means "plan."
6. a great work; The teacher *acceded*, so he agreed to give the students more time.
7. in a series of steps; People rehearse the scenes of plays *successively*.
8. admire it as an exceptional example of Gothic literature; Something that often *adorns* the hair of little girls is a hairclip or a bow.

Reading Warm-up B, p. 46
Sample Answers
   1. (well-known); We met the *illustrious* writer at a book-signing event.
   2. (detestable); Measles is an *odious* disease that causes pain and discomfort.
   3. the idea that emotion should be used to arrive at answers to questions; *Relinquished* means "gave up."
   4. (failing to follow these rules); I must *comply* with the rule of making my bed every morning.
   5. (Terror) (horror); The *incessant* knocking on the door was beginning to annoy me.
   6. terror as growing out of suspense; A monkey can use an *appendage*, such as its tail, to help it move through trees.
   7. a feeling in readers . . . event actually occurs; *Bestow* means "present as a gift or honor."
   8. (common saying); A *platitude* I have heard many times is, "The early bird catches the worm."

Literary Analysis: The Gothic Tradition, p. 47
Possible Responses
   1. The mountains and lake are beautiful, romantic, and mysterious. The constant rain adds an atmosphere of gloom and forces the poets indoors, where their thoughts turn to ghost stories.
   2. The ghost stories are filled with horrifying, gloomy details and deal with untimely deaths forced on the young with sorrowful irony.
   3. It is the product of her fevered imagination, which creates vivid images of a horrifying animated corpse. The images appear mysteriously, seeming to come out of thin air from "beyond the usual bounds of reverie." The descriptive language is varied and rich and terrifying: "pale student of unhallowed arts"; "hideous phantasm"; "uneasy, half vital motion"; "odious handiwork"; "horror-stricken"; "hideous corpse"; "horrid thing"; "yellow, watery . . . eyes."

Reading Strategy: Predict, p. 48

Suggested Responses

1. The story will be a hideous tale, perhaps shocking even to the author.

2. Her story *will* rival those stories they had been discussing. Additionally, the story will invoke some fear all humans have, possibly fears about death, life, personal identity, love, and so on.

3. Her story will dwell on the discovery and communication of life to a non-human.

4. Her nightmare that night will become the essence of *Frankenstein*.

Vocabulary Builder, p. 49

A. Sample Responses

1. imaginary; 2. ghost; 3. daydream; 4. place that exists only in the imagination; 5. bizarre and unbelievable

B. 1. acceded; 2. platitude; 3. phantasm; 4. ungenial; 5. incitement; 6. appendage

Grammar and Style: Past Participial Phrases, p. 50

A. 1. annoyed by the platitude of prose; circle *poets*

2. cradled in healthy sleep; circle *youths*

3. snapped from the stalk; circle *flowers*

4. left to itself; circle *spark*

B. Sample Responses

1. On Friday, all her best students, exhausted as they were by the test they had taken Thursday, were late to class.

2. The plants on Sara's windowsill, parched from neglect, withered and died.

3. Built in the eighteenth century, the house was more dilapidated than haunted.

4. Several of the stuffed animals, crowded onto the shelf above Magda's bed, were in danger of falling to the floor.

5. Samuel, angered by the loss of his ticket, did not listen to the train conductor's announcements and consequently missed his stop.

Enrichment: Science, p. 53

Sample Responses

1. using DNA evidence to prove that someone accused of a crime is guilty or innocent; taking soil samples from the moon or from Mars; laser surgery; splitting the atom; using a computer to model possible outcomes of a particular event

2. Students should suggest a plot based on twentieth-century technology or an imaginary extension of twentieth-century technology: for example, Shelley might write a novel about a scientist who discovers how to make it possible for people to live forever.

Selection Test A, p. 54

Critical Reading

1. ANS: B	DIF: Easy	OBJ: Comprehension
2. ANS: B	DIF: Easy	OBJ: Reading Strategy
3. ANS: D	DIF: Easy	OBJ: Comprehension
4. ANS: C	DIF: Easy	OBJ: Comprehension
5. ANS: B	DIF: Easy	OBJ: Interpretation
6. ANS: A	DIF: Easy	OBJ: Literary Analysis
7. ANS: C	DIF: Easy	OBJ: Comprehension
8. ANS: D	DIF: Easy	OBJ: Literary Analysis
9. ANS: A	DIF: Easy	OBJ: Literary Analysis

Vocabulary and Grammar

10. ANS: A	DIF: Easy	OBJ: Vocabulary
11. ANS: C	DIF: Easy	OBJ: Vocabulary
12. ANS: D	DIF: Easy	OBJ: Grammar

Essay

13. Students should mention that the Gothic elements of the vision include the dreadful idea of putting together a being out of body parts and using some fantastic machine to give it life. At first, the idea seems logical. But the plot quickly moves beyond science into the supernatural when the corpse takes on a life of its own. Shelley does not describe the setting, but she hints at a Gothic mood and tone when she tells how the monster stands beside the inventor's bedside.

Difficulty: *Easy*

Objective: *Literary Analysis*

14. Students should know that Byron, Percy Bysshe Shelley, Mary Shelley, and John Polidori each attempted to write stories. Byron finished only a fragment. (Percy) Shelley struggled to write the story. Polidori began a story based on a terrible idea and finally gave it up. Only Mary Shelley finished her story. Students may suggest that Polidori was not an experienced writer. Byron and Percy Shelley were poets, not writers of prose. They may have given up out of impatience. Mary Shelley had the best luck, perhaps because she felt inferior to Byron and Shelley, who were famous poets, and was therefore more motivated to try harder and to stay with her project.

Difficulty: *Easy*

Objective: *Essay*

Selection Test B, p. 57

Critical Reading

1. ANS: C	DIF: Average	OBJ: Interpretation
2. ANS: C	DIF: Easy	OBJ: Comprehension
3. ANS: D	DIF: Average	OBJ: Literary Analysis
4. ANS: C	DIF: Average	OBJ: Interpretation
5. ANS: A	DIF: Average	OBJ: Literary Analysis

6.	ANS: D	DIF: Challenging	OBJ: Reading Strategy
7.	ANS: B	DIF: Easy	OBJ: Interpretation
8.	ANS: C	DIF: Easy	OBJ: Reading Strategy
9.	ANS: A	DIF: Average	OBJ: Interpretation
10.	ANS: C	DIF: Average	OBJ: Reading Strategy
11.	ANS: B	DIF: Average	OBJ: Literary Analysis
12.	ANS: A	DIF: Average	OBJ: Literary Analysis

Vocabulary and Grammar

13.	ANS: C	DIF: Average	OBJ: Vocabulary
14.	ANS: B	DIF: Easy	OBJ: Vocabulary
15.	ANS: A	DIF: Average	OBJ: Grammar
16.	ANS: D	DIF: Challenging	OBJ: Grammar

Essay

17. Students' essays should compare *Frankenstein* with a contemporary work that explores the theme of technology used for the wrong purposes. For example, students might compare *Frankenstein* with *Jurassic Park,* a novel and movie that explores the possibility that scientists might find a way to clone dinosaurs from dinosaur DNA. If so, students might note that just as *Frankenstein* was inspired by public interest in the experiments of Dr. Erasmus Darwin, *Jurassic Park* was inspired by scientific attempts to clone one animal from the cell of another animal.

Difficulty: *Average*

Objective: *Essay*

18. Students' essays should identify characteristics of the Gothic novel that make it a part and product of the Romantic Age. For example, Gothic literature grew out of the Romantic denial of the Age of Reason's claim that everything could be explained scientifically.

Difficulty: *Challenging*

Objective: *Essay*

Poetry of William Wordsworth

Vocabulary Warm-up Exercises, p. 61

A.
1. region
2. uncertain
3. assist
4. orchard
5. glimpses
6. gentle
7. inward
8. duties

B. Sample Answers
1. F; You would live alone, because *seclusion* means "isolation."
2. T; *Adhered* means "followed."

3. F; It is better to research the car you want to buy because it is an expensive purchase.
4. T; *Bliss* means "joy."
5. F; *Judgments* are "opinions formed by evaluation," and they are made by judges.
6. F; *Opinions* are "beliefs or ideas that are not supported by direct proof."
7. T; *Summoned* means "convened."
8. T; *Majestic* means "showing great dignity," and a crown exemplifies this idea.

Reading Warm-up A, p. 62

Sample Answers
1. (apple); *Orchard* means "land used for growing fruit or nut trees."
2. (area); The southern *region* of the country usually has warm weather during the summer.
3. kept us cool in the summer sun; *Gentle* means "mild."
4. supervising a large staff and reporting important issues directly to the company's president; *Duties* means "obligations."
5. not sure; Sally was unfamiliar with this city, and she was *uncertain* about how to find the hotel.
6. (helped); I will *assist* the elderly woman in crossing the street.
7. faraway cities; *Glimpses* means "quick, incomplete views or looks."
8. a small lake populated by many varieties of birds; *Inward* means "located inside."

Reading Warm-up B, p. 63

Sample Answers
1. (beautiful); The majestic horse was admired by all who saw it.
2. Wordsworth's mother died when he was about eight years old.
3. began the English Romantic Movement; *Judgments* means "opinions based on reason."
4. they used everyday language and fresh ways of looking at nature; *Adhered* means "followed."
5. later became strained; *Opinions* means "beliefs not supported by direct proof."
6. to write some of his most famous poetry; *Summoned* means "called together."
7. He carefully constructed his poems to reflect the beauty he saw around him. *Impulse* means a sudden inclination to act.
8. he was surrounded by family and influential friends who visited him; *Seclusion* means "isolation."

Literary Analysis: Romanticism, p. 64

Suggested Responses
1. He describes his younger self as being like a roe. By comparing himself to an animal, he may be implying that

before he grew up, he—and perhaps all young people—were more a part of nature.

2. No; Wordsworth felt that people had become too far removed from nature and he was saying—undoubtedly rhetorically—that it would be better to err in the other direction, to believe in pagan nature gods, than to ignore nature completely.

Reading Strategy: Use Literary Context, p. 65

Possible Responses

2. "that serene and blessed mood, / In which the affections gently lead us on" ("Tintern Abbey," lines 41–42)—These lines deal with emotions rather than with intellect and reason.

3. "O sylvan Wye! . . . / How often has my spirit turned to thee!" ("Tintern Abbey," lines 56–57)—The Wye valley is a special place to the narrator because of his personal connection to it.

4. "While here I stand, not only with the sense / Of present pleasure, but with pleasing thoughts / That in this moment there is life and food / For future years." ("Tintern Abbey," lines 62–65)—These lines describe an emotional rather than a rational response.

5. "Oh! yet a little while / May I behold in thee what I was once, / My dear, dear Sister!" ("Tintern Abbey," lines 119–121)—These lines describe a personal rather than a universal experience.

Vocabulary Builder, p. 66

A. Sample Responses

1. to dissect or separate body parts for study
2. a scalpel or other type of knife
3. their internal organs
4. It analyzes the details of the crime.

B. 1. A; 2. A; 3. B; 4. C; 5. D; 6. B; 7. D

Grammar and Style: Present Participial Phrases, p. 67

A. 1. yes
2. No, because it is one word, not a phrase.
3. No, because *beatings* is used as a noun rather than an adjective, so it is not a participle.
4. yes
5. No, because it is one word, not a phrase.

B. Sample Responses

1. Walking to school, I lost my key.
2. That dog sitting over there looks like my dog.
3. The car rolling down the hill is out of control.
4. The man sitting next to me seems familiar.
5. The movie playing downtown is great!

Enrichment: Social Studies, p. 70

A. Sample Responses

1. I spend all day inside a dark, noisy, smelly factory in the middle of a big city. My father and grandfather worked in their shoemaking shop surrounded by trees in a small village.

2. I keep a machine running. I never see what the machine produces. Anyone could do the same job that I do. When my father or grandfather made a shoe, he took pride in it. No one else made a shoe exactly like theirs.

3. Being separated from nature and working in a job that anyone could do, a factory worker would probably identify with the way the poem stressed the importance of the individual and of nature.

B. Suggested Responses

Students' timelines might include works by Wordsworth, Coleridge, Byron, Keats, or Shelley, and such inventions as Samuel Crompton's spinning mule (1779), James Watts's steam engine (1782), William Horrocks's all-metal loom (1803), or Richard Trevithick's steam locomotive (1803).

Selection Test A, p. 71

Critical Reading

1. ANS: A	DIF: Easy	OBJ: Comprehension
2. ANS: C	DIF: Easy	OBJ: Comprehension
3. ANS: B	DIF: Easy	OBJ: Interpretation
4. ANS: D	DIF: Easy	OBJ: Literary Analysis
5. ANS: C	DIF: Easy	OBJ: Interpretation
6. ANS: B	DIF: Easy	OBJ: Reading Strategy
7. ANS: D	DIF: Easy	OBJ: Comprehension
8. ANS: C	DIF: Easy	OBJ: Literary Analysis
9. ANS: A	DIF: Easy	OBJ: Reading Strategy

Vocabulary and Grammar

10. ANS: A	DIF: Easy	OBJ: Vocabulary
11. ANS: C	DIF: Easy	OBJ: Vocabulary
12. ANS: B	DIF: Easy	OBJ: Grammar

Essay

13. Students should recognize that when Wordsworth first visited the area around Tintern Abbey, he was very young and his feelings toward nature reflected a pure, unquestioning joy and enthusiasm for it. He has become more thoughtful and finds nature a source of peace and inspiration. His response to nature has changed by it becoming even more important to him.

Difficulty: *Easy*

Objective: *Essay*

14. Students may point out that Wordsworth uses the simple, direct language of everyday speech. Although he discusses abstract ideas, he expresses them in language that is easy to understand. His diction, however, does include more difficult terms that make his feelings specific. Wordsworth also expresses strong feelings in all his poems, but perhaps most obviously in *The Prelude*, when he talks about his feelings about the Revolution. He also expresses strong responses to nature, especially in "Lines Composed a Few Miles Above Tintern Abbey," when he compares his earlier and current feelings toward nature.

Difficulty: *Easy*
Objective: *Essay*

Selection Test B, p. 74

Critical Reading

1. **ANS:** B	**DIF:** Average	**OBJ:** Interpretation
2. **ANS:** A	**DIF:** Challenging	**OBJ:** Reading Strategy
3. **ANS:** D	**DIF:** Average	**OBJ:** Comprehension
4. **ANS:** C	**DIF:** Average	**OBJ:** Intepretation
5. **ANS:** D	**DIF:** Average	**OBJ:** Interpretation
6. **ANS:** A	**DIF:** Easy	**OBJ:** Literary Analysis
7. **ANS:** C	**DIF:** Average	**OBJ:** Literary Analysis
8. **ANS:** A	**DIF:** Average	**OBJ:** Comprehension
9. **ANS:** D	**DIF:** Challenging	**OBJ:** Reading Strategy
10. **ANS:** A	**DIF:** Easy	**OBJ:** Interpretation
11. **ANS:** A	**DIF:** Challenging	**OBJ:** Reading Strategy
12. **ANS:** A	**DIF:** Average	**OBJ:** Literary Analysis

Vocabulary and Grammar

13. **ANS:** D	**DIF:** Easy	**OBJ:** Vocabulary
14. **ANS:** B	**DIF:** Average	**OBJ:** Vocabulary
15. **ANS:** B	**DIF:** Average	**OBJ:** Grammar
16. **ANS:** C	**DIF:** Easy	**OBJ:** Grammar

Essay

17. Students should describe Wordsworth's concern that people had come to be too much involved with society and making money and did not appreciate life and nature enough. They may cite such examples as his statement that he'd rather worship Greek nature gods than ignore nature the way others of his time did. Student opinions will vary, but many will probably agree that these concerns are as relevant to our own time as they were to Wordsworth's.

Difficulty: *Average*
Objective: *Essay*

18. Students should describe the change in the narrator's feelings at Tintern Abbey from the carefree wildness of a young boy to the more sober reflections of a grown man. They should also describe the change in Wordsworth's

own feelings regarding the French Revolution—from believing it to be a change for the better to the realization that the new regime was at least as bad as the old. The two works are similar in that they describe changes that come with age and experience, but they are different in that "Tintern Abbey" evokes a more general, universal experience while the selection from *The Prelude* is very specific and personal.

Difficulty: *Challenging*
Objective: *Essay*

Benchmark Test 7, p. 77

MULTIPLE CHOICE

1. **ANS:** C
2. **ANS:** A
3. **ANS:** B
4. **ANS:** D
5. **ANS:** A
6. **ANS:** C
7. **ANS:** B
8. **ANS:** D
9. **ANS:** A
10. **ANS:** D
11. **ANS:** A
12. **ANS:** D
13. **ANS:** B
14. **ANS:** C
15. **ANS:** B
16. **ANS:** A
17. **ANS:** C
18. **ANS:** C
19. **ANS:** A
20. **ANS:** A
21. **ANS:** C
22. **ANS:** A
23. **ANS:** D
24. **ANS:** D
25. **ANS:** B
26. **ANS:** C
27. **ANS:** D
28. **ANS:** A

ESSAY

29. Students should identify the characters and the works in which they appear. They should then briefly detail the similarities and differences between the two characters, citing details from the poems to support general statements about the characters. Students may organize their writing point by point, or they might fully discuss first one character and then the other.

30. Students should identify the work and describe their impressions of it before they read or saw it and explain the source of those impressions. They should then describe the ways in which the actual work lived up to or fell short of their expectations. They should cite specific details to support general statements about the work.

31. Students should restate the quotation and then explain it, discussing what it means for Romantic literature not to be concerned with exact truth and describing the feeling to which Baudelaire refers. Students should also consider whether or not they agree with Baudelaire's statement, especially the idea that Romanticism does not involve a particular subject matter. Some students may feel that nature poetry and Gothic literature do demand a particular subject matter.

Diagnostic Test 8, p. 83

MULTIPLE CHOICE

1. ANS: C
2. ANS: A
3. ANS: D
4. ANS: B
5. ANS: A
6. ANS: C
7. ANS: B
8. ANS: C
9. ANS: A
10. ANS: C
11. ANS: B
12. ANS: A
13. ANS: D
14. ANS: B
15. ANS: C

"The Rime of the Ancient Mariner" and "Kubla Khan" by Samuel Taylor Coleridge

Vocabulary Warm-up Exercises, p. 87

A.
1. ancient
2. harbor
3. glorious
4. sheen
5. pleasure
6. blossomed
7. merry
8. burst

B. Sample Answers

1. T; *Plagued* means "annoyed."
2. T; *Prayer* means "an act of communion with God or another deity in the form of confession, praise, or thanksgiving."

3. F; *Mariner* means "sailor," and he or she would sail a ship.
4. T; *Agony* means "intense physical or emotional pain," and you would feel this if you broke a bone.
5. F; *Din* means "great noise," and a library is usually very quiet.
6. F; *Chasm* means "a deep crack."
7. T; *Mingled* means "mixed."
8. T; *Howled* means "cried loudly."

Reading Warm-up A, p. 88

Sample Answers

1. (beauty); The tailor created the *glorious* evening gown for the queen.
2. crystal blue water; cruise ships that were anchored there; The ship sailed into the *harbor* to escape the storm at sea.
3. fragrance filling the air; *Blossomed* means "bloomed."
4. have existed for hundreds of years; *Ancient* means "very old."
5. poverty in which many of the island's residents lived; *Sheen* means "sparkling brightness."
6. (enjoyment); Watching an opera gives me great *pleasure*.
7. the suffering that was really there; *Merry* means "jolly."
8. her views about the island; *Burst* means "came about suddenly."

Reading Warm-up B, p. 89

Sample Answers

1. words, images, and phrases; *Din* means "a mix of loud, confusing, and disagreeable noises."
2. (sailor); The *mariner* sailed around the world on his ship.
3. are severely punished; *Plagued* means "distressed."
4. in great detail; *Agony* means "suffering."
5. The sailors had no water to drink; *Howled* means "cried loudly."
6. Water, water everywhere and not a drop to drink; *Mingled* means "mixed."
7. Coleridge tried to bridge the *chasm* between ideas and ways to express them; *Chasm* means "divide."
8. took a great interest in philosophy; *Prayer* means "act of communion with God or another deity."

Literary Analysis: Poetic Sound Devices, p. 90

1. consonance; 2. assonance; 3. alliteration;
4. internal rhyme; 5. consonance; 6. alliteration;
7. assonance; 8. internal rhyme; 9. assonance;
10. alliteration; 11. alliteration; 12. alliteration;
13. alliteration; 14. assonance

Reading Strategy: Analyze Poetic Effects, p. 91
Sample Responses

2. "About, about, in reel and rout / The death fires danced at night. . . ." ("Rime," lines 127–128) Internal rhyme and alliteration. Internal rhyme in the words *about* and *rout* emphasizes the rhythmic, omnipresent nature of the death fires. Alliteration of *reel* and *rout* and of *death* and *danced* draws attention to the key words in this passage.

3. "'A speck, a mist, a shape, I wist! / And still it neared and neared. . . .'" ("Rime," lines 153–154) Alliteration, internal rhyme, and repetition. Alternation of the alliteration of *speck* and *shape* with the internal rhyme of *mist* and *wist* produces the sense that the ship is coming closer, as does the repetition of *neared* and *neared*.

4. "'Alone, alone, all, all alone, / Alone on a wide wide sea!'" ("Rime," lines 232–233) Repetition and alliteration. Repetition of the words *alone, all,* and *wide* emphasizes the Mariner's horror at being the only one left alive, and alliteration of the *w* sound creates a hissing noise like a howling wind.

5. "'Farewell, farewell! but this I tell / To thee, thou Wedding Guest!'" ("Rime," lines 610–611) Repetition, internal rhyme, and alliteration. Repetition of the word *farewell* alerts the reader that the Mariner is about to give his final comments, while internal rhyme of *farewell* and *tell* and alliteration of *this, thee,* and *thou* create a rhythm that draws the reader to pay particular attention.

Vocabulary Builder, p. 92

A. 1. journey; 2. journalism; 3. journal; 4. adjourn; 5. du jour

B. 1. A; 2. D; 3. B; 4. D; 5. A; 6. B

Grammar and Style: Inverted Word Order, p. 93

A. 1. The subject (*an Albatross*) and verb (*did cross*) have been inverted.

At length an Albatross did cross.

2. The prepositional phrase (*about my neck*) precedes what it modifies (*hung*) instead of following it.

Instead of the cross, the Albatross was hung about my neck.

3. The subject (*mingled measure*) and verb (*was heard*) are inverted.

Where the mingled measure was heard from the fountain and the caves.

4. The verb (*saw*) and its direct object (*damsel with a dulcimer*) are inverted.

Once I saw in a vision a damsel with a dulcimer. . . .

B. Sample Responses

1. In that light saw I a sprite.

2. Around the pole his fingers wrapped; that it would snap I knew.

3. Up the walk ran the man and his dog, the injured bird to fetch.

4. Into my ears slipped music soft and sent me right to sleep.

Enrichment: Science, p. 96
Suggested Responses

A. 1. Students might list fantastic, nightmarish elements such as the skeleton ship, the waking dead sailors, and the haunting, lingering quality of the dead albatross from "The Rime of the Ancient Mariner," and the dancing rocks and the sunny ice caves from "Kubla Khan."

2. Students should refer to the "damsel with a dulcimer" seen by the narrator "in a vision." As the narrator remembers this dream, he feels that if he could only recall her song, he would be delighted and inspired by it. Students might then note that there seems to be a parallel between the song the narrator heard in his dream and the text of "Kubla Khan," which Coleridge heard in his own dream.

Suggested Responses

B. Students should report on a specific aspect of the scientific study of dreams, and should include information that has been proven scientifically.

Selection Test A, p. 97
Critical Reading

1. ANS: C	DIF: Easy	OBJ: Comprehension	
2. ANS: B	DIF: Easy	OBJ: Literary Analysis	
3. ANS: B	DIF: Easy	OBJ: Interpretation	
4. ANS: A	DIF: Easy	OBJ: Reading Strategy	
5. ANS: D	DIF: Easy	OBJ: Comprehension	
6. ANS: D	DIF: Easy	OBJ: Literary Analysis	
7. ANS: A	DIF: Easy	OBJ: Interpretation	
8. ANS: B	DIF: Easy	OBJ: Interpretation	
9. ANS: A	DIF: Easy	OBJ: Literary Analysis	

Vocabulary and Grammar

10. ANS: C	DIF: Easy	OBJ: Vocabulary
11. ANS: A	DIF: Easy	OBJ: Vocabulary
12. ANS: B	DIF: Easy	OBJ: Grammar

Essay

13. Students should know that the pleasure dome was built by Kubla Khan somewhere in China. They might describe it as a huge garden surrounded by a wall with towers. Inside was a river, gardens, and ancient forests. They might also describe the deep chasm where the woman wailed for her demon lover and how the earth heaved up the river in a huge fountain. Students might choose any of these aspects of the poem as the most memorable or interesting.

Difficulty: *Easy*

Objective: *Comprehension*

14. Students should observe that the sound devices enhance the beauty and emotional impact of "The Rime of the Ancient Mariner" by creating musical effects. Without the sound devices, the poem would tell a curious story but would not be as memorable or engaging. The sound devices help readers share a stronger sensory experience of the story. Because the sensory experience is stronger, the emotional response of the reader is also stronger.

Difficulty: *Easy*

Objective: *Essay*

Selection Test B, p. 100

Critical Reading

1. ANS: D	DIF: Average	OBJ: Literary Analysis
2. ANS: A	DIF: Easy	OBJ: Interpretation
3. ANS: C	DIF: Average	OBJ: Literary Analysis
4. ANS: D	DIF: Challenging	OBJ: Reading Strategy
5. ANS: A	DIF: Average	OBJ: Comprehension
6. ANS: C	DIF: Average	OBJ: Interpretation
7. ANS: C	DIF: Average	OBJ: Literary Analysis
8. ANS: C	DIF: Average	OBJ: Comprehension
9. ANS: B	DIF: Average	OBJ: Reading Strategy
10. ANS: C	DIF: Average	OBJ: Literary Analysis
11. ANS: B	DIF: Average	OBJ: Reading Strategy

Vocabulary and Grammar

12. ANS: A	DIF: Easy	OBJ: Vocabulary
13. ANS: D	DIF: Easy	OBJ: Vocabulary
14. ANS: D	DIF: Challenging	OBJ: Grammar
15. ANS: C	DIF: Average	OBJ: Grammar

Essay

16. Students should describe the elements of fantasy that Coleridge ascribes to Xanadu, pointing to such details as the spirit of the "woman wailing for her demon lover" and the vision of the Abyssinian maid "singing of Mount Abora." Students may also point out that a love of the exotic is naturally suited to the Romantic temperament, which revels in the mystery of the unknown and all that lies outside the realm of everyday experience.

Difficulty: *Average*

Objective: *Essay*

17. Students' answers should note that these lines explain why the Mariner's voyage became so disastrous after he killed the albatross—the Polar Spirit was taking revenge on him. Some students may note that the Mariner's problems, created by the Polar Spirit's love for the albatross, can only be resolved when the Mariner himself

begins to feel love for the natural world. Students should identify the assonance created by the *i* sound in the first line and the simple repetition of words in the third line (*loved . . . loved*). The stark simplicity of these lines produces a lonely tone that, some students may suggest, implies that lack of appreciation for nature results in loneliness and disconnectedness.

Difficulty: *Challenging*

Objective: *Essay*

"She Walks in Beauty," from *Childe Harold's Pilgrimage* and from *Don Juan*
by George Gordon, Lord Byron

Vocabulary Warm-up Exercises, p. 104

A. 1. ambition
2. treasure
3. express
4. squandered
5. impaired
6. conceal
7. innocent
8. praise

B. Sample Answers
1. F; A *bard* is a poet.
2. F; *Invincible* means "unbeatable."
3. T; *Azure* means "the color blue."
4. T; *Aspect* means "facial expression."
5. F; *Gaudy* means "showy in a tasteless way."
6. T; *Eloquent* means "movingly expressive."
7. T; *Despise* means "dislike intensely."
8. T; *Spurning* means "scorning;" this is not a good thing to do if you need help.

Reading Warm-up A, p. 105

Sample Answers
1. struggled to make ends meet; *Innocent* means "blameless."
2. young Byron grew up in poverty; *Squandered* means "wasted."
3. it received almost universally bad reviews; *Praise* means "expression of approval."
4. (communicate); It is important to learn how to *express* yourself in writing.
5. as many people there disagreed with his views; *Impaired* means "diminished in strength or quality."
6. Byron left England permanently and settled in Switzerland and later Italy; *Conceal* means "hide."
7. (*Don Juan*); *Treasure* means "valuable" or "precious possessions."
8. (objective); My *ambition* is to sail around the world.

Reading Warm-up B, p. 106

Sample Answers

1. Byron's colorful personality also made him famous; *Eloquent* means "movingly expressive."

2. eccentric, unconventional, flamboyant, and controversial; *Azure* means "the color blue."

3. While he gracefully described the romance of the azure skies and unrequited love in his poetry; *Bard* means "poet."

4. his sympathy for victims; *Aspect* means "the way a person or thing looks or is seen."

5. (bullies); *Despise* means "dislike intensely."

6. Byron was not *invincible* because he died before he had the opportunity to fight; *Invincible* means "unbeatable."

7. he supported many liberal causes; *Spurning* means "scorning."

8. monkeys, cats, peacocks, geese, a badger, a parrot, a heron, and his beloved dog, Boatswain; *Gaudy* means "showy."

Literary Analysis: Figurative Language, p. 107

A. 1. personification; 2. metaphor; 3. simile; 4. personification; 5. simile

B. Sample Responses

1. The storm clouds glowered over the trembling town.

2. Courage blanketed his anxious fears.

3. A feeling of peacefulness washed over her like a spring rain.

4. His thoughts roared to her doorstep on the wheels of his dreams.

Reading Strategy: Question, p. 108

Sample Responses

1. Who is the speaker of the poem?
   A thirty-year-old man

2. What is the subject of this excerpt?
   The subject is the speaker's reflections on the meaning of his life and what will remain of him after he has died.

3. What does the speaker think of fame?
   He considers it to be overrated.

4. Why does the speaker think that he has wasted his youth?
   He apparently spent it partly on love affairs and drinking, and partly writing poetry.

5. Why does the speaker quote Southey at the end of this excerpt?
   He's making fun of Southey, and thinks that if Southey can be remembered, certainly he (the speaker) could be, too.

Vocabulary Builder, p. 109

A. 1. delicious; 2. adventurous, ominous; 3. famous, humorous; 4. miraculous; 5. rebellious

B. 1. F; 2. A; 3. C; 4. D; 5. B; 6. G; 7. I; 8. E; 9. H

Grammar and Style: Subject-Verb Agreement, p. 110

A. 1. agree; 2. tell; 3. is; 4. are, melt; 5. Has dried; 6. agree

B. Sample Responses

1. A raindrop falls on the mountain and begins its rush to the sea.

2. A professional dancer usually attends classes every day.

3. Coffee and tea are best served hot.

4. Olives can be put on top of pizza, pressed into oil, or even baked in bread.

5. The two strangers did not know where to buy tokens for the subway.

Enrichment: Film Portrayal of Don Juan, p. 113

Sample Responses

Opening Scene

Plot: This is a version of the poem adapted to modern times. The narrator, an older man, is reading one of his own books. Then he begins to reminisce about his youth. He states that as a young man, he had two missions: to have affairs with beautiful women, and to become famous.

Location: A library

Supporting Characters: None

The Narrator as a Young Man

Plot: We learn that the narrator has accomplished both his missions, but they have not brought him satisfaction. The women he meets either turn out to be unappealing to the narrator in some comical way, or they dump him. On his way to the Isle of fame, he conquers the beasts of Writer's Block and Stale Ideas. He works late into the night writing poetry and does become famous, but poetry critics appear on television and offer scathing criticisms of his work.

Selection Test A, p. 114

Critical Reading

1. ANS: A	DIF: Easy	OBJ: Interpretation
2. ANS: D	DIF: Easy	OBJ: Reading Strategy
3. ANS: C	DIF: Easy	OBJ: Reading Strategy
4. ANS: B	DIF: Easy	OBJ: Interpretation
5. ANS: B	DIF: Easy	OBJ: Literary Analysis
6. ANS: A	DIF: Easy	OBJ: Literary Analysis
7. ANS: B	DIF: Easy	OBJ: Comprehension
8. ANS: A	DIF: Easy	OBJ: Literary Analysis
9. ANS: D	DIF: Easy	OBJ: Interpretation
10. ANS: B	DIF: Easy	OBJ: Comprehension

Vocabulary and Grammar

11. ANS: C	DIF: Easy	OBJ: Vocabulary
12. ANS: D	DIF: Easy	OBJ: Vocabulary
13. ANS: A	DIF: Easy	OBJ: Grammar

Essay

14. Students should recognize that figurative language is used in all three poems, but it is used most in the excerpt from *Child Harold's Pilgrimage*. This poem makes frequent use of personification of the ocean. Students may, because of the personification, decide that *Child Harold's Pilgrimage* makes the most memorable use of figurative language. However, students might also argue that the most memorable figurative language occurs in the opening line of "She Walks in Beauty."

Difficulty: *Easy*

Objective: *Essay*

15. Students should note that the speaker in *Don Juan* says that he has lived a full life in just a few years, and at age thirty, he has exhausted much of his enthusiasm. In the process, he has come to realize life is short and fame is brief and not as rewarding as he once thought. Students may or may not agree with this philosophy, but should give reasons for their positions.

Difficulty: *Easy*

Objective: *Essay*

Selection Test B, p. 117

Critical Reading

1. ANS: B	DIF: Average	OBJ: Interpretation
2. ANS: A	DIF: Easy	OBJ: Reading Strategy
3. ANS: C	DIF: Average	OBJ: Literary Analysis
4. ANS: D	DIF: Easy	OBJ: Comprehension
5. ANS: C	DIF: Average	OBJ: Reading Strategy
6. ANS: B	DIF: Average	OBJ: Literary Analysis
7. ANS: B	DIF: Average	OBJ: Interpretation
8. ANS: B	DIF: Challenging	OBJ: Interpretation
9. ANS: C	DIF: Challenging	OBJ: Reading Strategy
10. ANS: B	DIF: Average	OBJ: Literary Analysis
11. ANS: D	DIF: Average	OBJ: Interpretation

Vocabulary and Grammar

12. ANS: C	DIF: Average	OBJ: Grammar
13. ANS: A	DIF: Easy	OBJ: Grammar
14. ANS: B	DIF: Easy	OBJ: Grammar
15. ANS: B	DIF: Average	OBJ: Vocabulary
16. ANS: D	DIF: Average	OBJ: Vocabulary

Essay

17. Students' essays should identify traits of a person that the speaker attributes to the ocean. For example, the speaker states that the ocean hates the destruction that humans wreak on land.

Difficulty: *Average*

Objective: *Essay*

18. Students' essays should compare the ways in which the speakers of "She Walks in Beauty" and *Childe Harold's Pilgrimage* elevate their subjects with the ways in which the speaker of *Don Juan* makes fun of himself. For example, the speakers of the first two poems compare their subjects to things that are eternal— night and "the Almighty"—while the speaker of *Don Juan* compares his life to something that is easily and quickly used up— money.

Difficulty: *Challenging*

Objective: *Essay*

"Ozymandias," "Ode to the West Wind," and "To a Skylark" by Percy Bysshe Shelley

Vocabulary Warm-up Exercises, p. 121

A.
1. antique
2. hues
3. solid
4. keen
5. scattering
6. decay
7. surpass
8. prophecy

B. Sample Answers
1. F; *Colossal* means "huge."
2. T; *Commotion* means "agitation," and this can occur during football games.
3. F; *Dirge* means "a funeral hymn."
4. T; *Visage* means "a person's face or appearance."
5. F; A *sculptor* creates three-dimensional designs.
6. F; *Tumult* means "a great disturbance."
7. T; *Wanderings* means "meanderings," and you can discover new things this way.
8. T; *Boyhood* means "a man's childhood."

Reading Warm-up A, p. 122

Sample Answers
1. politically conservative climate of the England in which he was raised; My mother loves to search flea markets for *antique* toys.
2. Shelley would develop a strong dislike of tyranny; My *prophecy* for Shelley, if he hadn't died so young, would be that he would become a member of the House of Commons, as well as a poet.

3. in his writing; *Keen* means "sharp."

4. Shelley met influential politicians and read about important issues; Someone without a *solid* political foundation might act as though the workings of the government didn't affect him or her at all.

5. throughout England and Ireland: Yes. At election time, my mailbox and front step are covered with political pamphlets, which shows that politicians still are in the habit of *scattering* their literature to potential voters.

6. (deterioration); The *decay* of the wood was caused by the moisture.

7. should be permitted to participate in political life—In other words, everyone should have a voice . . .; *Hues* means "colors."

8. many of his writer contemporaries for its beauty, style, and content; A runner wants to always *surpass* his best sprinting time.

Reading Warm-up B, p. 123

Sample Answers

1. because of his inate talent, and in part, due to the efforts of his wife . . . to enhance and perceive his literary reputation; The truck coming up behind me on the highway is *colossal*, dwarfing in size all the other cars and trucks near it.

2. (relationship); The couple's argument caused a *commotion* in the quiet restaurant.

3. They were both political radicals and free thinkers; If Shelley's *boyhood* had been a happy, he might have felt that the status quo was perfectly fine.

4. throughout Europe; After their *meanderings*, they returned to England, where they . . .

5. (elopement); *Tumult* means "great disturbance."

6. The two created worlds of fiction and poetry—carefully, as though molding clay; Like her husband, Mary was a careful *molder* of images and words.

7. Shelley's funeral was untraditional . . .ceremony on the beach.

8. they do recognize and appreciate his words; To this day, though people may not recognize Shelley's expressive *face* from likenesses, they do recognize and appreciate his words.

Literary Analysis: Imagery, p. 124

Sample Responses

1. sight, touch (one might imagine touching the sand or the sculpture)

2. curiosity, possibly fear or resentment of the "sneer of cold command"

3. sight, touch, hearing (The wreck is probably surrounded by noticeable silence, because there is nothing else there except a vast expanse of desert.)

4. awe that nothing remains of the civilization except the wreck, or satisfaction that this dictatorial ruler is no longer remembered or recognized

5. This passage illustrates that even a totalitarian ruler cannot command time, and eventually his dictatorial rule will pass into oblivion.

Reading Strategy: Respond to Imagery, p. 125

Sample Responses

2. "Angels of rain and lightning: there are spread / On the blue surface of thine aery surge, / Like the bright hair uplifted from the head / Of some fierce Maenad. . . ." ("West Wind," lines 18–21) Description: The sky is blue but it is possible to see the storm approaching in the distance, where it is already raining. One can hear and smell the approaching rain and feel the damp wind. Senses: sight, smell, touch

3. "Scatter, as from an extinguished hearth / Ashes and sparks, my words among mankind!" ("West Wind," lines 66–67) Description: The image is of a fireplace in which a fire has recently gone out, and the wind kicks up still hot ashes and sparks. Senses: sight, smell, hearing

4. "Like a highborn maiden / In a palace tower, / Soothing her love-laden / Soul in secret hour / With music sweet as love, which overflows her bower . . ." ("Skylark," lines 41–45) Description: The image is a castle tower from which one can hear a young woman's sweet song. Senses: sight, hearing

5. "Like a rose embowered / In its own green leaves, / By warm winds deflowered, / Till the scent it gives / makes faint . . ." ("Skylark," lines 51–55) Description: A rose bud stays contained with the greenery of a bush until winds cause the flower to open and lose its odor. Senses: sight, smell, hearing (the sound of wind)

Vocabulary Builder, p. 126

A. 1. pulsar; 2. compulsive; 3. impulsiveness; 4. repulse

B. 1. sepulcher; 2. profuse; 3. vernal; 4. visage; 5. satiety, verge; 6. blithe; 7. impulse

Grammar and Style: Subjunctive Mood, p. 127

A. The following verbs should be underlined:

If I *were* a dead leaf . . .;

If I *were* a swift cloud . . .;

I *were* as in my boyhood, and *could be* . . .

I *would ne'er have striven*. . . .

B. Sample Responses

1. That apple should not fall far from the tree.

2. Samantha could hurt herself if she loses her balance on those slippery steps.

3. I wish you were happier about this decision.

4. Marty would not resign from the company.

5. Bruno could not talk, even if he wanted to—he's only a dog.

Enrichment: Meteorology, p. 130

Suggested Response

Students should report on a specific field of meteorology. For example, climatologists make statistical analyses of trends in such areas as sunlight, humidity, rainfall, and wind, all elements of climate that may affect food production or ocean temperature. Such scientists also study fossils of plants to determine how the climate in an area has changed. Such information is of use in agriculture, aviation, and public health. To get a starting job, a climatologist needs a bachelor's degree in meteorology, engineering, geography, or computer science.

Selection Test A, p. 131

Critical Reading

1. ANS: A	DIF: Easy	OBJ: Comprehension
2. ANS: C	DIF: Easy	OBJ: Interpretation
3. ANS: D	DIF: Easy	OBJ: Interpretation
4. ANS: B	DIF: Easy	OBJ: Literary Analysis
5. ANS: D	DIF: Easy	OBJ: Reading Strategy
6. ANS: A	DIF: Easy	OBJ: Literary Analysis
7. ANS: B	DIF: Easy	OBJ: Reading Strategy
8. ANS: A	DIF: Easy	OBJ: Comprehension
9. ANS: C	DIF: Easy	OBJ: Comprehension

Vocabulary and Grammar

10. ANS: D	DIF: Easy	OBJ: Vocabulary
11. ANS: A	DIF: Easy	OBJ: Vocabulary
12. ANS: C	DIF: Easy	OBJ: Grammar

Essay

13. Students should mention that the message of "Ozymandias" is the temporary nature of human power. The image of the trunkless legs of the statue supports the message. The head and torso are half buried in the sand. Another image is the sneering expression on the face of the statue that is also lying in the sand. The final image is of a vast desert of sand. In every direction, the speaker is saying, nothing remains to show the power of this king.
Difficulty: *Easy*
Objective: *Essay*

14. Students should note that in "To a Skylark," Shelley uses expansive imagery to show the freedom and beauty of the skylark's flight and its song. Some of the imagery suggests how far above humans the skylark can fly. We know it is there even though we cannot see it. In the final stanzas, Shelley makes the connection clearer, as he specifically compares the joy of the skylark to joy that humans experience that is always edged with sorrow.
Difficulty: *Easy*
Objective: *Essay*

Selection Test B, p. 134

Critical Reading

1. ANS: C	DIF: Average	OBJ: Interpretation
2. ANS: B	DIF: Easy	OBJ: Comprehension
3. ANS: B	DIF: Easy	OBJ: Literary Analysis
4. ANS: A	DIF: Challenging	OBJ: Interpretation
5. ANS: A	DIF: Average	OBJ: Comprehension
6. ANS: C	DIF: Average	OBJ: Interpretation
7. ANS: B	DIF: Average	OBJ: Reading Strategy
8. ANS: A	DIF: Average	OBJ: Literary Analysis
9. ANS: C	DIF: Average	OBJ: Comprehension
10. ANS: B	DIF: Average	OBJ: Reading Strategy
11. ANS: D	DIF: Average	OBJ: Interpretation
12. ANS: A	DIF: Easy	OBJ: Literary Analysis
13. ANS: A	DIF: Challenging	OBJ: Interpretation
14. ANS: C	DIF: Easy	OBJ: Reading Strategy

Vocabulary and Grammar

15. ANS: B	DIF: Average	OBJ: Vocabulary
16. ANS: C	DIF: Average	OBJ: Grammar

Essay

17. Students' essays should note that the speaker admires the destructive force of the West Wind because it makes new beginnings possible, and that Shelley seems to be suggesting that death is a necessary part of life. For example, the wind carries seeds to their cold graves, but in the spring, the seeds will sprout and grow.
Difficulty: *Average*
Objective: *Essay*

18. Students' essays should identify the speaker's problem as a kind of writer's block. The speaker is frustrated with his work and hopes for the wind to help scatter his "dead thoughts" and produce the conditions that are necessary for him to have a creative "Spring." For example, the speaker asks the wind to make him its lyre.
Difficulty: *Challenging*
Objective: *Essay*

Poetry of John Keats

Vocabulary Warm-up Exercises, p. 138

A.
1. rhyme
2. pursuit
3. realms
4. dissolve
5. brim
6. passion
7. fame
8. immortal

B. Sample Answers

1. F; *Cease* means "to stop."
2. F; *Legend* means "an unverified popular story that is handed down."
3. T; Climbing a mountain in that way is *perilous*, or "dangerous."
4. T; Cairo, Egypt is located *abroad*, or in a foreign country.
5. T; *Relish* means "to enjoy."
6. F; *Lustrous* means "shiny," and velvet is not shiny.
7. T; A positive *attitude*, or disposition, helps you to accomplish difficult tasks.
8. F; *Forlorn* means "lonely because of abandonment."

Reading Warm-up A, p. 139

Sample Answers

1. after his death; *renown*
2. He engaged in this lifelong pursuit in the face of these difficulties; *Passion* means "zeal."
3. in the face of these difficulties; *Pursuit* means "activity."
4. he decided to train to become a surgeon; *Realms* means "areas."
5. he read widely while he was in school, and he wrote his first poem, "Lines in Imitation of Spenser," in 1814; *disintegrate*
6. he was ill with the same disease that killed his brother, Tom; *Immortal* means "not subject to death."
7. with beautiful images; *Brim* means "edge."
8. gave him the renown he never had while he was alive; *Rhyme* means "the correspondence of sounds at the ends of words."

Reading Warm-up B, p. 140

Sample Answers

1. the images and rich language; *enjoy*
2. (love); *Attitude* means "disposition."
3. the deepest meaning of life was found in the understanding of the lustrous beauty surrounding him; *Lustrous* means "radiant."
4. due to his failing health and his sadness over his brother's death; *Forlorn* means "lonely because of abandonment."
5. notes that the beauty of the urn will never *cease*, as it is permanently captured within its art; The *legend* of the horseman of Sleepy Hollow has existed for hundreds of years.
6. The beauty of the urn is permanently captured in its art; *continue, persist*
7. He attempted to overcome this illness by moving abroad to Italy in order to live in a warmer climate; The pioneers began their *perilous* journey across the uncharted desert.
8. (Italy); *Abroad* means "in a foreign country."

Literary Analysis: Ode, p. 141

"Ode to a Nightingale"

8 stanzas; 10 lines in each stanza; rhyme scheme is *abab cdecde*; meter is iambic pentameter, with iambic trimeter in eighth line of each stanza; it is a Horatian ode.

"Ode on a Grecian Urn"

5 stanzas; 10 lines in each stanza; rhyme scheme is *abab cdecde*, except for the first stanza: *abab cdedce*, and the second stanza: *abab cdeced*; meter is iambic pentameter; it is a Horatian ode.

Reading Strategy: Paraphrase, p. 142

Sample Responses

1. When I fear that I might die before I've written down the ideas that fill my brain . . .
2. Fade away, dissolve, and forget the weariness, sickness, and worry that you have never known while living in the leaves.

Vocabulary Builder, p. 143

A. 1. quality of draining or being drained; 2. state of being married or wed; 3. state of being bound or tied up; 4. state of being in short supply; 5. state of being wrecked or broken

B. 1. surmise; 2. gleaned; 3. requiem; 4. vintage; 5. teeming; 6. ken

Grammar and Style: Direct Address, p. 144

A. 1. Thou still unravished bride of quietness Thou foster child of silence and slow time, Sylvan historian
2. Fair youth
3. happy, happy boughs!
4. O Attic shape! Fair attitude!
5. Thou, silent form . . . Cold Pastoral!

B. Sample Responses

1. O thoughtless man, I wish I could forget you and your wicked birds.
2. Some day, misguided folk, you will all see that I'm no child, that I knew the truth.
3. If only you would look my way, old friend, you'd know my mind.
4. Great, towering castle, I wonder what secrets hide behind those bricks of yours.
5. Sweet, gentle form, did you know that the sight of you knocks me speechless?

Enrichment: Greek Art, p. 147

Suggested Responses

A. 1. Students should write a general description of figures depicted on the vase.
2. Students should name the figures and explain their significance in ancient Greek mythology, history, or lifestyle.

B. Students' designs should show an understanding of the ancient Greeks while depicting scenes from today. Student explanations should demonstrate thought given to the design and an attention to its details.

Selection Test A, p. 148

Critical Reading

1. **ANS:** A	**DIF:** Easy	**OBJ:** Interpretation
2. **ANS:** C	**DIF:** Easy	**OBJ:** Comprehension
3. **ANS:** D	**DIF:** Easy	**OBJ:** Literary Analysis
4. **ANS:** A	**DIF:** Easy	**OBJ:** Reading Strategy
5. **ANS:** B	**DIF:** Easy	**OBJ:** Reading Strategy
6. **ANS:** B	**DIF:** Easy	**OBJ:** Literary Analysis
7. **ANS:** C	**DIF:** Easy	**OBJ:** Comprehension
8. **ANS:** D	**DIF:** Easy	**OBJ:** Reading Strategy

Vocabulary and Grammar

9. **ANS:** B	**DIF:** Easy	**OBJ:** Vocabulary
10. **ANS:** D	**DIF:** Easy	**OBJ:** Vocabulary
11. **ANS:** B	**DIF:** Easy	**OBJ:** Grammar

Essay

12. Students should understand that the main idea of the poem is summarized in the final lines of the poem that clearly states that beauty is truth and truth is beauty. Students should identify and explain at least three images. They might point out that the young lover never gets to kiss his beloved, but on the other hand, his love never dies, and his beloved's beauty never fades. The tree limbs never lose their leaves, and spring never passes. In the final stanza, the speaker summarizes the frozen stances of the figures and explains that they will last forever even though the people of this generation die. In other words, art remains.

Difficulty: *Easy*

Objective: *Essay*

13. Students should mention that in "Ode to a Nightingale," Keats describes the song and flight of the nightingale. He admires the joy expressed in the nightingale's song and how that song has not changed since ancient times. In "Ode on a Grecian Urn," Keats describes the picture on an ancient Grecian urn. Like the nightingale's song, the picture is timeless. It was just the same in ancient times and will be the same when the present generation is long gone. Although both subjects appear timeless, the speaker responds differently to each. The nightingale causes him to think about his own mortality and cares, whereas the Grecian urn helps him realize the purity and enduring power of art.

Difficulty: *Easy*

Objective: *Essay*

Selection Test B, p. 151

Critical Reading

1. **ANS:** C	**DIF:** Average	**OBJ:** Interpretation
2. **ANS:** D	**DIF:** Average	**OBJ:** Comprehension
3. **ANS:** B	**DIF:** Challenging	**OBJ:** Reading Strategy
4. **ANS:** D	**DIF:** Average	**OBJ:** Interpretation
5. **ANS:** C	**DIF:** Average	**OBJ:** Interpretation
6. **ANS:** D	**DIF:** Average	**OBJ:** Comprehension
7. **ANS:** A	**DIF:** Easy	**OBJ:** Literary Analysis
8. **ANS:** C	**DIF:** Easy	**OBJ:** Literary Analysis
9. **ANS:** B	**DIF:** Average	**OBJ:** Literary Analysis
10. **ANS:** C	**DIF:** Challenging	**OBJ:** Reading Strategy
11. **ANS:** D	**DIF:** Easy	**OBJ:** Reading Strategy
12. **ANS:** A	**DIF:** Average	**OBJ:** Interpretation

Vocabulary and Grammar

13. **ANS:** B	**DIF:** Easy	**OBJ:** Vocabulary
14. **ANS:** C	**DIF:** Challenging	**OBJ:** Vocabulary
15. **ANS:** B	**DIF:** Challenging	**OBJ:** Vocabulary
16. **ANS:** B	**DIF:** Easy	**OBJ:** Grammar
17. **ANS:** D	**DIF:** Average	**OBJ:** Grammar

Essay

18. When comparing the two odes, students should refer to passages and details from the text to support their arguments. They may note that he considers the figures painted on the urn to be free of some human constraints, but the nightingale has earthly cares, sickness, and even death. The figures on the urn are free from the stealing, punishing passage of time. The eternal youth and springtime of the urn painting, however, seem to inspire him to ecstatic admiration, whereas the nightingale causes him to reflect heavily on his own mortality and cares.

Difficulty: *Average*

Objective: *Essay*

19. Students may note that Keats regards immortality with wonderment and admiration, and that the enduring quality of art and literature probably plays an important role in his appreciation of them. His own mortality, on the other hand, is a source of worry and sorrow. In "On First Looking Into Chapman's Homer," for example, students might point out that while he does not speak directly of immortality, he is impressed by the grandeur of Homer as expressed by Chapman; Homer's greatness has lasted for centuries, and Keats's exposure to this literature expands his own horizons on a universal level. Students might then note that "When I Have Fears That I May Cease to Be" shows Keats's great fear that he will not live long enough to write everything he wants to write. It may seem to them that to leave behind great works represents his only chance at immortality.

Difficulty: *Challenging*
Objective: *Essay*

"Speech to Parliament: In Defense of the Lower Classes" by George Gordon, Lord Byron
"A Song: 'Men of England'"
by Percy Bysshe Shelley
"On the Passing of the Reform Bill"
by Thomas Babington Macaulay

Vocabulary Warm-up Exercises, p. 155

A.
1. bankruptcy
2. fluctuating
3. speculate
4. fraud
5. impediments
6. deference
7. ferocity
8. reformed

B. Sample Answers
1. F; *Felony* means "a serious crime," so it is not a good deed.
2. T; *Exalted* means "lifted up," and that is the position of the military leader.
3. F; *Terminate* means "to bring to an end," and a dead-end street does have an end.
4. T; *Prescriptions* are necessary to buy some medications.
5. F; *Famished* means "extremely hungry," so a famished person would want more food.
6. T; *Majority* means "more than half of a group," and most of the people in the United States do own telephones.
7. T; *Emancipate* means "to free from oppression," and freeing the slaves was one of the reasons the Civil War was fought.
8. F; *Accomplices* means "associates in wrongdoing," so those working for charity would not usually be called accomplices.

Reading Warm-up A, p. 156

Sample Answers
1. the way people produced goods; *Reformed* means "changed for the better."
2. in the nineteenth century; A word that means about the same as *ferocity* is *fierceness*.
3. (stood in the way); An antonym to *impediments* is "help."
4. afford to look to the future; Many telecommunications businesses declared *bankruptcy* in the years 2000 and 2001.
5. (theft); A person who commits *fraud* might be arrested and sent to jail.

6. (think); Although no one saw him do it, many people *speculate* that Matt played the prank at the school dance.
7. reverence; A person who typically receives *deference* from others is the President of the United States.
8. (stable); The price of gold was *fluctuating* because the market was not stable.

Reading Warm-up B, p. 157

Sample Answers
1. high-flying; Something that is often *exalted* in the United States is stardom.
2. government's leaders; It means "associates in wrongdoing."
3. (crimes); Stealing a car is a *felony* that is punishable by imprisonment.
4. feed; A word that means about the same as *famished* is *starving*.
5. (misery); International organizations work to *emancipate* groups of people who are being oppressed around the world.
6. a relatively small part of the population; A *majority* vote means that more than half of the organization's members must agree before a new rule can be put in place.
7. (the poor); *Prescriptions* means "suggested or authorized treatments."
8. (prolong); A charity organization might work to *terminate* people's suffering by offering food, clothing, shelter, and other aid to those who need it.

Literary Analysis: Political Commentary, p. 158

Possible Responses
1. Shelley encourages "the Men of England" to recognize that they are exploited and controlled by their employers. He indicates that they should consider the possibility of armed revolt against their masters.
2. The poet hopes to raise the consciousness—if not the weapon-bearing arm—of the "common men" of England.
3. Not only is poetry Shelley's preferred form, but a "song" can also be easily read, understood, memorized, and recited. Rhyming verses such as these could be useful to workers trying to unite and protest as a group.
4. Shelley's intended audience includes the vast multitudes of manual laborers all across England.
5. Shelley uses simple vocabulary—such as *plough, weave, feed, clothe, cradle, food, seed, cellars*—to describe the tasks and objects of working-class British life in the early years of the Industrial Revolution.

Reading Strategy: Set a Purpose for Reading, p. 159

Sample Responses
Purpose: to learn about the lives of nineteenth-century working-class people in England; Passages: (1) "Men of England, wherefore plough / For the lords who lay ye low?" (lines 1–2)—

Farmers toiled for upper-class lords; (2) "Wherefore feed and clothe . . . / Those ungrateful drones who would / Drain your sweat—nay, drink your blood?" (lines 5–8)—The upper class treated the working class poorly; (3) "Have ye leisure, comfort, calm, / . . . Or what is it ye buy so dear / With your pain and with your fear?" (lines 13–16)— The working class probably did not live comfortable lives with sufficient leisure time; (4) "Forge arms—in your defense to bear." (line 24)—The working class may have been kept unarmed to prevent a revolution.

Vocabulary Builder, p. 160

A. 1. C; 2. D; 3. B; 4. E; 5. A
B. 1. C; 2. B; 3. B; 4. D; 5. A; 6. B

Grammar and Style: Correlative Conjunctions, p. 161

A. 1. . . . both Shelley and Byron
2. . . . whether Lord Byron is considered a Romantic or a Victorian
3. Neither Byron nor Shelley
4. Just as repetition can underscore a poem's musicality, so too can it intensify
5. . . . contains not only examples of Shelley's verses, but also a selection

B. Sample Responses
1. You may write your research report on the life and literary works of either Percy Bysshe Shelley or Mary Shelley.
2. Poets must consider carefully not only the connotations but also the sounds of the words they choose to express their ideas.
3. Whether you are writing a speech or a persuasive essay, you must pay close attention to your audience.

Enrichment: Political Commentary, p. 164

Sample Responses
1. I believe that the school system should decrease spending on athletics and increase spending on classroom materials for students.
2. Since I hope to publish this piece of writing in the school newspaper, my audience will include high-school students, faculty members, administrators, and parents. This audience represents both genders and a wide range of ages and special interests. Many people in this audience will probably have strong feelings about this topic, so I will need to be fair and balanced in my arguments.
3. I think it would be most effective to draft my commentary as an "open letter" to the school community.
4. I should strike a straightforward, assertive, but not aggressive tone, in order not to alienate any readers who feel that athletics are of great value to students. I should use informal language—as I would use in a personal letter—yet I should avoid slang, sarcasm, or technical terms that some readers might not understand.

5. Given the nature of my topic, I think an organization using main ideas and details would be most effective.

Selection Test A, p. 165

Critical Reading

1. ANS: B	DIF: Easy	OBJ: Comprehension
2. ANS: C	DIF: Easy	OBJ: Comprehension
3. ANS: D	DIF: Easy	OBJ: Reading Strategy
4. ANS: A	DIF: Easy	OBJ: Literary Analysis
5. ANS: B	DIF: Easy	OBJ: Literary Analysis
6. ANS: C	DIF: Easy	OBJ: Reading Strategy
7. ANS: A	DIF: Easy	OBJ: Interpretation
8. ANS: D	DIF: Easy	OBJ: Literary Analysis

Vocabulary and Grammar

9. ANS: A	DIF: Easy	OBJ: Vocabulary
10. ANS: C	DIF: Easy	OBJ: Vocabulary
11. ANS: D	DIF: Easy	OBJ: Grammar

Essay

12. Students should recognize that Shelley uses several nature images. In one, he compares bees to the men of England. The worker bees are the English workers who feed and cloth the drones, who are the privileged class. In another image, he compares the seeds that workers sow to the work they do. He says the workers plant the seed, but others—the privileged—harvest the crop. Students may say the images are very effective in painting a picture of how hard the men of England work while others get most of the benefit.
    Difficulty: *Easy*
    Objective: *Essay*

13. Students should note that Byron argues that the bill proposed in Parliament to punish weavers for destroying their looms is much too severe. He points out that the weavers were losing their jobs and were no longer able to earn their livings. He reasons that the wealthy commit crimes such as fraud, bankruptcy, and felonies when they are in trouble, so members of Parliament should not expect better behavior from the weavers. Parliament should be working to improve the poor working conditions, not considering the death penalty as punishment. Most students will say that Byron's arguments are convincing.
    Difficulty: *Easy*
    Objective: *Essay*

Selection Test B, p. 168

Critical Reading

1. ANS: C	DIF: Average	OBJ: Comprehension
2. ANS: B	DIF: Average	OBJ: Interpretation

3. ANS: D	DIF: Average	OBJ: Literary Analysis
4. ANS: B	DIF: Easy	OBJ: Reading Strategy
5. ANS: C	DIF: Average	OBJ: Interpretation
6. ANS: D	DIF: Challenging	OBJ: Literary Analysis
7. ANS: A	DIF: Easy	OBJ: Reading Strategy
8. ANS: C	DIF: Average	OBJ: Interpretation
9. ANS: C	DIF: Average	OBJ: Literary Analysis
10. ANS: D	DIF: Easy	OBJ: Reading Strategy
11. ANS: B	DIF: Average	OBJ: Literary Analysis

Vocabulary and Grammar

12. ANS: B	DIF: Easy	OBJ: Vocabulary
13. ANS: A	DIF: Easy	OBJ: Vocabulary
14. ANS: B	DIF: Average	OBJ: Grammar
15. ANS: D	DIF: Average	OBJ: Grammar

Essay

16. Students should make a considered judgment about the images' effectiveness and explain why they are more or less appropriate in Byron's speech. For instance, to support the idea that Byron's images of food and war are crucial to the success of his speech, a student might argue that the weavers' hunger was literal and real— and that the force of laws protecting mere property ought to pale in contrast with human starvation.

Difficulty: *Average*

Objective: *Essay*

17. Students should make a clear statement about what they deem the appropriate relationship between art and politics. The view that politics and art are rightly mixed could be supported, for instance, by citing evidence of Shelley's not sacrificing artistic quality while enlightening his audience and inciting social change. Students who hold the view that politics and art are best kept separate might support their idea with references to Byron's "Speech to Parliament: In Defense of the Lower Classes." By using oratorical and rhetorical devices (rather than poetic devices oriented toward aesthetics), Byron makes the most forceful political argument possible.

Difficulty: *Challenging*

Objective: *Essay*

"On Making an Agreeable Marriage"
by Jane Austen

from *A Vindication of the Rights of Woman*
by Mary Wollstonecraft

Vocabulary Warm-up Exercises, p. 172

A. 1. conviction
2. conscientiously
3. amiable

4. uniformly
5. partial
6. deficiencies
7. comprehension
8. attribute

B. Sample Answers

1. F; If you *deplore* chocolate ice cream, you do not like it.
2. F; *Prevalent* means "commonly occurring." There are no trees in the Sahara Desert.
3. F; *Degraded* means "reduced in rank or status."
4. T; You would need strength to deal with the stress of a life-threatening situation.
5. F; Comedians tell their jokes with a sense of humor, not seriousness.
6. F; *Frivolous* means "silly," which means that such hobbies would not be necessary.
7. T; A sense of balance is what *equilibrium* means.
8. T; Scientists need to be able to reason in order to prove their theories.

Reading Warm-up A, p. 173

Sample Answers

1. to her parents' support of her efforts; *Attribute* means "relate to a particular cause or source."
2. that she could do anything if she put her mind to it; *Conviction* means "unshakable belief."
3. carefully; *carelessly, thoughtlessly*
4. read outside of class; I have a poor *comprehension* of Spanish because I speak very little of it outside the classroom.
5. (Preferring); I love acting and am *partial* to the drama club.
6. she seldom attended the school dances because of her intense study schedule; The product was not sold to the public because it contained many dangerous *deficiencies*.
7. (consistently); *differently, unevenly*
8. (friendly); The *amiable* dog wagged its tail as we pet it.

Reading Warm-up B, p. 174

Sample Answers

1. that women were inferior to men; *Prevalent* means "widely occuring."
2. debasing treatment; *Degraded* means "reduced in rank or status."
3. (silly); The dress had many *frivolous* details on it, such as ribbons and bows.
4. this type of silly behavior; If I *deplore* beans, I will not eat them often because I do not like them.
5. capable of the same intellectual achievements; *Rational* means "having the ability to reason."
6. (strength); Climbing Mount Everest requires great physical strength and *fortitude*.
7. Nearly two centuries after her death

8. (serious); *insignificance, triviality*

Literary Analysis: Social Commentary, p. 175
Sample Responses

1. Austen points out that many people are made happier by the chase than they are by the conquest. She points out that her niece is hopelessly in love until she wins the devotion of the object of her desire. Then she promptly loses interest in him.

2. Wollstonecraft asserts that society breeds women for nothing more than childish pursuits, when actually the raising of children and the running of a household are pursuits that require educated, mature processing skills.

Reading Strategy: Determine the Writer's Purpose, p. 176
Sample Responses

Paragraph 2: Although her tone is still sad, Wollstonecraft addresses her subject matter-of-factly.—The author's purpose is to heap more facts on top of her argument.—Wollstonecraft is embittered by the fact that a woman of her day can't rise through any means except marriage. This is less of a factor today, depending upon where women live.

Paragraph 3: The author appeals to the rational side of men by suggesting rather sarcastically that women should become more like men so that they can in turn command the respect of men.—The author's purpose is to point up the absurdity of the current situation.—The author is making a strong point.

Paragraph 4: The author's tone is incredulous. She uses strong words like *bugbear, fortitude,* and *prejudices.*—The author seeks to appeal to men's sense of fair play.—Since the whole piece is about fair play, this is an excellent path to take.

Paragraph 5: The author's tone is firm.—Her message is clear: Give women a chance and let them prove whether or not they deserved that chance.—Although things have improved for some women today, there are still times when women are held back from success. Everyone should be treated equally.

Vocabulary Builder, p. 177

A. Sample Responses

1. in a loud, strong way; 2. strongly barricaded;
3. strengthen; 4. strong attempt

B. 1. solicitude; 2. specious; 3. gravity; 4. vindication;
5. fastidious; 6. fortitude; 7. preponderates;
8. scruple; 9. amiable

Grammar and Style: Commas in a Series, p. 178
A. 1. Fanny and her friends and family addressed the problem of her impending marriage.
2. correct

3. Mary Wollstonecraft felt that young women were taught to behave in a deceptive, conniving(,) and ridiculous way.

B. Sample Responses

1. Women were expected to be pleasant, cunning, and pretty.

2. Large families produced male heirs, strong workers, and women who seemed to have no real place in the world.

3. Jane Austen, though unmarried herself, expected others to marry based on love, honor, and trust.

Enrichment: Social Studies, p. 181
Sample Responses

1. Since the young couple never spent time alone together, they probably didn't know each other all that well when they later married.

2. The custom of a man's money passing to his eldest male heir could cause a number of problems within the family. There could be jealousy among the siblings. A selfish or malicious male heir might make his sisters suffer. And since women were not educated to work for a living, being left penniless was an ongoing fear, and reality.

3. Students may say that today women enjoy the same freedom to pursue their self-development that men do. However, some may suggest that although things are better now than they were in Wollstonecraft and Austen's time, women still do not have full equality. They may make less money than men working in comparable jobs, and there are fewer women than men working in powerful high-paying jobs.

Selection Test A, p. 182
Critical Reading

1. ANS: C	DIF: Easy	OBJ: Comprehension
2. ANS: B	DIF: Easy	OBJ: Reading Strategy
3. ANS: D	DIF: Easy	OBJ: Comprehension
4. ANS: C	DIF: Easy	OBJ: Interpretation
5. ANS: B	DIF: Easy	OBJ: Literary Analysis
6. ANS: A	DIF: Easy	OBJ: Reading Strategy
7. ANS: B	DIF: Easy	OBJ: Comprehension
8. ANS: C	DIF: Easy	OBJ: Comprehension

Vocabulary and Grammar

9. ANS: C	DIF: Easy	OBJ: Vocabulary
10. ANS: D	DIF: Easy	OBJ: Vocabulary
11. ANS: B	DIF: Easy	OBJ: Grammar

Essay
12. Students should note that according to Austen's letter, some of the best qualities in a husband included wealth,

intelligence, and amiability. She also suggested finding a husband who had good habits, high principles, and good manners. Austen thought all of these qualities were important, but she thought it was even more important to marry someone a woman loved, or at least felt affection for.

Difficulty: *Easy*

Objective: *Essay*

13. Students should recognize that Austen's social commentary is unconscious. She is writing a letter to her niece to advise her on a suitor. Her intent is not to discuss customs but her niece's specific situation. Wollstonecraft's commentary, on the other hand, is conscious. She is analyzing social customs regarding the role women have been placed in by society. Both writers make many of the same assumptions: Women and men have different roles in society, men provide the homes and livelihood, and women succeed through the success of their husbands. Wollstonecraft challenges these assumptions and urges change. Austen simply analyzes them without really taking a position.

Difficulty: *Easy*

Objective: *Essay*

Selection Test B, p. 185

Critical Reading

1. ANS: D	DIF: Average	OBJ: Comprehension
2. ANS: D	DIF: Challenging	OBJ: Literary Analysis
3. ANS: B	DIF: Challenging	OBJ: Reading Strategy
4. ANS: C	DIF: Average	OBJ: Literary Analysis
5. ANS: B	DIF: Challenging	OBJ: Literary Analysis
6. ANS: C	DIF: Average	OBJ: Comprehension
7. ANS: A	DIF: Easy	OBJ: Reading Strategy
8. ANS: B	DIF: Challenging	OBJ: Reading Strategy
9. ANS: C	DIF: Easy	OBJ: Interpretation

Vocabulary and Grammar

10. ANS: D	DIF: Average	OBJ: Vocabulary
11. ANS: B	DIF: Easy	OBJ: Vocabulary
12. ANS: B	DIF: Easy	OBJ: Vocabulary
13. ANS: C	DIF: Average	OBJ: Grammar
14. ANS: D	DIF: Average	OBJ: Grammar

Essay

15. Students' essays may compare such things as Austen's mention of the need to marry "the eldest son of a Man of Fortune" with Wollstonecraft's assertion that the only way a woman could rise in the world was through marriage. They may make use of more subtle comparisons, such as Austen's mention of her recently married friend, Anna. Austen states that she is glad Anna doesn't parade her happiness and behave in a silly manner over her marriage. Wollstonecraft spends much of her essay addressing

women's silly behavior over men and over life in general. The two authors' styles are in stark contrast with each other. Students should contrast Austen's gentleness of manner and her coaxing style with Wollstonecraft's strong assertions and more instructive style.

Difficulty: *Average*

Objective: *Essay*

16. Students may or may not feel that Wollstonecraft's style is blunt by today's standards. Whichever answer they choose, their essays should provide support for their point of view.

Difficulty: *Challenging*

Objective: *Essay*

Writing About Literature—Unit 4

Evaluate Literary Trends: Integrating Grammar Skills, p. 189

Sample Revisions

1. The democratic ideals of the French Revolution inspired the Romantics to champion the dreams and problems of the common people.

2. The suffering caused by industrialization provoked the Romantics to reject a faith in science and reason.

3. The Romantics believed that the wildness and freedom of nature could inspire people to discover their own sense of freedom.

4. The Romantics promoted the values of simplicity, emotion, and individuality.

5. The Romantics explored the relationship between fantasy and reality, and they believed that the power of the imagination could transform our experience of life.

6. The Romantics believed people could discover truth, not through scientific analysis, but by using the power of imagination and fantasy.

Writing Workshop—Unit 4

Job Portfolio and Résumé: Integrating Grammar Skills, p. 191

A. 1. active
2. passive
3. passive
4. active
5. active

B. 1. I assist the coach of a middle-school football team.
2. I recruit and train tutors for an after-school study club.
3. I make donuts for a local bakery.
4. I assist customers in a shoe store.
5. I take phone orders at a pizza shop.

Spelling—Unit 4

Proofreading Practice, p. 192

1. famous; 2. symphonic; 3. writing; 4. startling;
5. originality; 6. passionate; 7. prodigious;
8. recognized; 9. reliance; 10. running; 11. marvel;
12. hemmed; 13. aspired; 14. succeed; 15. exercises;
16. flexibility; 17. novel; 18. proceeded;
19. professional; 20. realized; 21. senses;
22. pseudonym; 23. precarious; 24. daringly;
25. criticized; 26. expressiveness

Benchmark Test 8, p. 195

MULTIPLE CHOICE

1. ANS: A
2. ANS: B
3. ANS: D
4. ANS: A
5. ANS: D
6. ANS: C
7. ANS: A
8. ANS: C
9. ANS: B
10. ANS: C
11. ANS: A
12. ANS: B
13. ANS: D
14. ANS: B
15. ANS: B
16. ANS: A
17. ANS: D
18. ANS: B
19. ANS: B
20. ANS: A
21. ANS: A
22. ANS: D
23. ANS: B
24. ANS: C
25. ANS: C
26. ANS: B
27. ANS: D
28. ANS: B
29. ANS: A
30. ANS: D
31. ANS: C
32. ANS: C

ESSAY

33. Students should demonstrate an understanding of symbolism and sensory detail. They should record three images with two or three sensory details each.

34. Students should demonstrate an understanding of monologue. They should be able to convey their ideas through the voice of a fictional character.

35. Students should demonstrate the ability to generate questions useful for researching the background of a poem and its topic.

36. Students should demonstrate an understanding of editorial structure and persuasive language. They should support their ideas with clear facts and logic.

37. Students should accurately sum up the reviewer's arguments and their differing opinions. Students' views should be supported by specific details.